PONDS:
Their Wildlife and Upkeep

By the same author:
Animal Senses

PONDS:
Their Wildlife and Upkeep

ROBERT BURTON

DAVID & CHARLES
Newton Abbot London North Pomfret (Vt) Vancouver

ISBN 0 7153 7390 0

Library of Congress Catalog Card Number 77-076100

Set in 11 on 13pt Baskerville
by Trade Linotype Ltd Birmingham
and printed in Great Britain
by Redwood Burn Limited
for David & Charles (Publishers) Limited
Brunel House Newton Abbot Devon

Published in the United States of America
by David & Charles Inc
North Pomfret Vermont 05053 USA

Published in Canada
by Douglas David & Charles Limited
1875 Welch Street North Vancouver BC

CONTENTS

All photographs are by Jane Burton with the exception of nos 1 and 40 which were taken by the author. The publishers acknowledge Bruce Coleman Ltd for the use of illustration 32.

1

INTRODUCING PONDS

There is something enchanting about water. It is the focus of the landscape, drawing us by its many moods; peaceful and serene with clear reflections, stormy and overcast offering violence, or flowing merrily, gurgling and sparkling down a watercourse. We read how a river entranced Mole in *The Wind in the Willows*, and provided the wherewithal for playing 'pooh-sticks' in *The House at Pooh Corner.* Still waters received Excalibur and trapped Narcissus. So from our earliest days we find rivers, lakes and ponds associated with storybook enchantment and adventure. How much more real this becomes if we have access to water, particularly in the form of small pools and streams that can be waded and thoroughly investigated. In the course of splashing about (the more spray and mud picked up the better) we would find small animals to excite at least casual interest, but for the most part, when young, water is for messing about in.

Many professional zoologists have started their careers as collectors of pond animals. Presumably they had a latent interest in wildlife, together with the determination, patience and curiosity to seek and enquire, and they found that ponds and streams had an advantage over plant pressing, egg collecting or bird watching as an introduction to the study of natural history. The advantages of the pond as a training ground are several. The fascination of the water itself cannot be overlooked; and ponds, pools and streams are universal. There are few parts of the country where there is no water nearby. Even city parks usually have ponds.

Another advantage is that ponds are accessible. By definition a pond is a small, shallow body of water, so it can be explored with a long-handled net whose range is extended by paddling, and it can be investigated thoroughly with little effort or outlay in expensive equipment. This leads us to a further advantage of the pond as a haunt for budding naturalists. A small pond, only a few yards across, may contain an incredible wealth of animal life. Within this volume of water there will be representatives of almost every class of living thing.

For most pond collectors, identifying their catch is only a start. They want to know more about their habits and way of life. So we are more concerned here with looking at the pond as a microcosm – a miniature, independent world – and examining the ways in which the pond's inhabitants are fitted for life in this tiny environment. In general, most pond animals have a common ancestry with land-living types and they have acquired changes in anatomy, physiology and behaviour that allow them to live in fresh water. The problems of an aquatic existence are the same for all animals but they have found different ways of overcoming them.

Studying the lives of pond animals brings us to a final advantage of embarking upon pond collecting. Pond animals can be kept easily either in proper aquaria or in makeshift jamjars and other containers. So they can be brought into the home and studied at leisure. The aquarium lets us eavesdrop on pond life. We can watch the animals' everyday lives in comfort, observing their breeding habits and their methods of feeding and avoiding being eaten in turn by bigger animals.

THE HISTORY OF PONDS

Before examining these pond animals in detail, we need to know more about the background of the pond. How did it come into existence and why are there so many small bodies of water scattered about the countryside? The history of ponds is, in itself, an absorbing study, because they have played a vital part in the economy of our ancestors from time immemorial until the early years of this century.

Ponds occur naturally in many ways. In the first instance, Ice Age glaciers deposited uneven piles of rock debris which blocked streams and left depressions that filled with water. Other ponds formed where limestone strata were dissolved away by water and the ground subsided, or they appeared as gaps in the dense mat of vegetation in swamps and bogs. A pond may also come into existence when a river alters course, cutting off part of the old channel which retains its water level. Gradually this channel changes its appearance from a scoured river bed to a pond by the growth of plants and accumulation of dead plant material that rots into mud in the still water. However, most ponds are man-made and date from the days of a simple rural economy. Nowadays they are obsolete because technological progress has left them as mere relics of bygone ways of life, along with disused canals and ripped-up railway lines. All three are now being preserved or regenerated for conservation and recreation purposes. The ponds that survive act as reservoirs of wildlife, a joy to behold if well managed and a source of pleasure and instruction for amateur naturalists and professional biologists alike.

What might be called the standard or text-book pond is the pond on the village green. It was not built to look picturesque but played a central part in village economy in the days before mains water. It provided water for domestic use if there was no pump; it also provided drinking water for animals. We forget just how many animals would have been on the roads then. Not only were there riding horses and draught animals pulling carriages and carts, there were herds of cattle, sheep, pigs and even geese on their way to and from market. They had to cover long distances and needed watering. As a result, the course of a road was often governed by the location of springs, streams and pools although special ponds might be dug at crossroads. A water supply and a road made a good meeting point and it is likely that many ponds came first and villages grew up round them.

1 A farm pond holding its water despite two dry summers. The willows are a shelter for birds and water voles leave trails through the duckweed

A single village often had several ponds along the length of its street and the whole parish would contain many more. Farm animals needed watering so there were more ponds by farmyards and the pasture lands, strategically placed so that one pond could be shared by animals in several fields. These ponds had an additional use in providing water for crops in dry summers. Loading watercarts must have been a tedious and time-consuming process but good ponds could give tons of water without drying up.

Where there were no springs or streams to supply water, the villagers and farmers had to rely on rainwater, either direct or from run-off. Their ponds had to be catchment reservoirs like the cisterns of Mediterranean countries. In Britain, there are few places where there is no source of underground water, or streams, although the severe drought of 1976 showed that these sources cannot always be relied on. An exception is the downland of southern England where underlying chalk quickly soaks up the rain. When the Downs were an important sheep-farming region, water was supplied by the so-called dewponds, to which a certain mystique still clings. Once thought to be extremely ancient relics of prehistoric times, dewponds were still being built in the 1930s and the oldest date back probably no further than Roman times.

It used to be thought that these ponds were filled by trapping dew and that their construction was a secret known to only a few men of certain country families. However, the technique of the dewpond is to dig a shallow saucer, some 20yd across and 6ft deep, and line it with clay, well puddled to make it waterproof and mixed with flints to form a solid floor for the hoofs of livestock. The pond is sited in a hollow so that the maximum amount of rain and surface run-off is trapped.

Although water supply was *the* vital function of village and farm ponds, they supplied two further requirements: food and power. In bygone days, before the introduction of feed crops such as turnips in the eighteenth century, most livestock had to be killed before winter. Winter fare therefore was poor and dull but, fortunately, ponds were a continual source of fish. The Church's prohibition of meat-eating during Lent and on Fridays further stimulated the rearing of fish for the table. Whilst village ponds no doubt doubled as fish ponds, manor houses and monasteries had their own stews – the name given to ponds specially used for keeping fish for the table. A moat made an excellent stew, the source of food being close at hand; an advantage no doubt doubly useful during a siege.

'Pond' comes from the same Anglo-Saxon word as 'pound' or 'pen' meaning an enclosure where animals are herded. So a pond in the strict sense is an enclosure for water made by damming a stream, and describes the ponds used to supply water power for the earliest industries. Waterwheels were being built to drive grain mills before the Norman Conquest and the mill ponds acted as reservoirs of energy while doubling as fish ponds. Later, the wheels drove bellows for fanning the furnaces used in iron manufacture. From medieval times until the Industrial Revolution, the centre of England's iron industry was in the Weald of Sussex, Kent and Surrey. Water power was so essential to this early industry that iron-making was restricted to those parts of the Weald where there were suitable streams for damming, even though the iron ore occurs over a much greater area. All that is left of this enterprise are a few peaceful hammer ponds, placenames such as Abinger Hammer and Hammer Bottom, and some derelict mills. The last main use of the village pond as a source of power was to provide water for steam-driven traction engines.

Apart from supplying water, food and power, ponds were also valuable as sources of clay and willow wands for the 'wattle and daub' walls of primitive housing and they provided rushes for 'rush-dips', the only form of lighting for the poorer people. Many ponds resulted from the need for building materials, being formed from abandoned and waterlogged sand and gravel pits or rock and slate quarries. Sandy farmland was once enriched by marling – the digging up of clay or chalk to spread over the fields. Many a farm pond must be a legacy of this process.

This brief summary obviously does not exhaust the list of origins and uses of ponds which even extended to the judicial side of village life where ducking miscreants was as good a rough and ready form of correction as the stocks. Some villages had special ducking stools so that the punishment of offenders could be administered in a controlled fashion, with the dignity that the law demanded. A macabre sideline was the use of the pond for judgement rather than punishment. Suspected witches were bound and thrown in. If they floated it was a sure sign that the pond rejected them and they were guilty of an association with the devil. If they sank, they were innocent, and with luck were rescued before they drowned.

The pond is therefore a rich treasury of ancient ways and folklore. It was an indispensable part of our ancestors' lives: there were once something like 350,000 ponds in England and Wales and even this is probably an underestimate. Since the motor age started in Edwardian times, the number has been shrinking as ponds fell into disuse and slowly grew over, a natural process which is described in Chapter 9. Others became a repository for rubbish. Indeed, a traditional village pond is nowadays hardly complete without the remains of a bicycle, a bedstead and an old boot or two. The water conveniently covers the junk, so it is 'out of sight, out of mind'. Infilling is often deliberate. A pond is an obstacle for farm machinery and is a source of disease for cattle so the government gives grants for filling in ponds. The village pond is frequently seen as an eyesore and an offence to the nose (which it now often is) or a hazard to life because children may fall in and drown. For these reasons, too, it is filled in.

2

WHAT MAKES A POND?

Fresh waters range from ephemeral puddles that last for a few hours after a heavy shower, through bird baths, ponds, lakes, gravel pits, rivers, canals to the huge inland seas of North America and East Africa. Each kind has its characteristic community of animals and plants; simple in a puddle but varied and complex in large lakes. We are concerned here with life of the smaller, shallower bodies of water which can be examined with wellingtons and dipping nets.

To understand and enjoy pond life we need some basic knowledge of its physical environment as the pond has various characteristics that profoundly affect what lives in it. Although this is a rather technical subject it is worth grasping its essentials as, in the long run, a little theoretical knowledge makes practical exploration so much more rewarding.

THE PHYSICAL ENVIRONMENT

Pond water is not just wet. It is a fluid with qualities essential for life, including vital gases in solution. No organism can live in absolutely pure water. Plants, for example, depend on carbon dioxide for growth. This is achieved by photosynthesis, the process in which energy from the sun is 'trapped' by using it to transform carbon dioxide and water into carbohydrate. As the carbon dioxide present in the atmosphere is readily soluble in water, plants are never short of this vital commodity which can be absorbed over their whole surface (p 96). Carbon dioxide is also produced as a by-product of respiration, the reverse process by which plants and animals liberate energy by oxidising carbohydrate or fat to carbon dioxide and water.

The oxygen needed for respiration is gathered either from the air or from solution and the amount of oxygen in any body of water depends on a variety of factors. Sewage pollution is harmful as the processes of decomposition require oxygen, so removing oxygen needed for animals and plants. As temperature rises, the oxygen-carrying capacity of water decreases so that warm water, while being favourable for growth by speeding body processes, may actually be disastrous because it does not contain sufficient oxygen to fuel these processes.

Oxygen supplies in water are replenished in two ways. Its absorption from the atmosphere is enhanced by stirring, as when running water cascades over boulders or through the action of wind. Secondly, plants release oxygen as a by-product of photosynthesis so that the gas may actually bubble out of the water in strong sunlight.

Dissolved salts in water vary greatly in quantity and character, depending on the rocks and soils over which the water flows or collects. 'Hard' water which leaves deposits of 'fur' in kettles and pipes, contains calcium and magnesium carbonates and is alkaline. 'Soft' water lacks these minerals and is acidic. Generally, the quality of life is richer in hard waters where the essential minerals promote plant growth, as do the common phosphate and nitrate fertilisers that are applied to farms and gardens. Two substances are particularly needed for the body growth of some pond life : calcium carbonate or lime is essential for the shells of snails, which are consequently less abundant in soft water, while diatoms, the minute plants that thrive in fresh waters, have shells of silica.

Fresh waters are usually divided into two categories of mineral abundance. Eutrophic waters – the name comes from the Greek words for 'good food' – are rich in the nutrients needed for plant growth. Ponds are likely to be eutrophic as they have amassed nutrients from the decay of plants and animal remains. By contrast, a highland tarn or lochan, or a new gravel pit, is oligotrophic, meaning 'poor food'. Such waters are deficient in nutrients either because they lie on hard, infertile rock or through newness. As some people find it hard to distinguish between the words eutrophic and oligotrophic, it may help to associate *eu*trophic with *eu*phoric as both refer to good or pleasing states of being.

One reason why this information is included is that a new word is being bandied about in conservation circles – eutrophication, which refers to conditions in ponds, lakes and rivers where too many nutrient salts kill off both plants and animals. These excessive nutrients stimulate a huge increase in plants which are unable to live as the water cannot supply enough oxygen for their need.

As the dead plants rot, the bacteria breaking down their tissues use up more oxygen. Water animals cannot live in these conditions so they, too, die and the water becomes stinking and lifeless. Eutrophication occurs when the water is enriched with raw sewage or with artificial fertilisers washed by rain from neighbouring fields.

Light penetration into water is vital for plants which need the sun's rays for photosynthesis. Water absorbs light so that even in the clearest pools, plant life can exist only in relatively shallow water. As soon as the water is contaminated with silt or peat, light penetration is greatly reduced.

Temperature affects the speed of life, and chemical processes speed up when the body is warmed. Thus an organism lives faster in a warmer environment, unless it is warm-blooded and can control its body temperature. For the most part, we are concerned here with cold-blooded animals – amphibians and reptiles, fishes and invertebrate animals – whose ability to control body temperature is limited. Aquatic animals, in particular, are tied to the temperature of the environment. They cannot lose heat by evaporation (sweating) and cannot increase their body temperature because heat liberated by body processes is immediately lost to the water. The result is that water animals have body temperatures no more than a fraction of a degree more or less than the surrounding water.

As warm water is less dense than cooler water, it rises to the surface, forming a top layer favourable to animals and plants. Water is a peculiar substance as it reaches a maximum density at 4°C then becomes less dense as temperature drops, whereas other fluids get progressively denser. So, when the surface of a pond begins to cool in autumn, the surface water sinks, warmer water below rises and is cooled in turn until the whole pond is at 4°C. Cooling continues but now the colder water floats on the surface and eventually a layer of ice is formed. If it were not for this unique property, a body of water would freeze as a solid mass rather than forming a sheet of ice. This would be inconvenient, to say the least, for the organisms living in it. As it is, they are protected from extremes of temperature by the ice preventing wind from mixing the upper cold layer of water with the warmer water below.

The density of water is very high when compared with air so animals must work hard to move through it (try wading in a hurry!). However, as water's density is about the same as that of protoplasm, minute plants and animals float effortlessly. (We can float because our density is reduced by two lungs full of air.) Any tendency to sink is counteracted by fine extensions of the body which act as parachutes. Water fleas develop projections on their bodies during the summer to help them float when the water is warmer and considerably less dense than in winter.

A final property of water that affects aquatic life is surface tension, the condition that makes a liquid behave rather as if it has an elastic sheet covering it. Its effects are more obvious if the fluid is in contact with an unwettable surface. On a polished metal surface, like that of a freshly washed and waxed motor car, for example, water is drawn into near spherical droplets because water molecules cling to each other rather than to the metal. The application of a detergent reduces the surface tension and the drops spread out. Insects that walk on the surface of water have unwettable bodies and the legs of insects such as pond skaters are provided with pads of fine hairs at the tips which spread their weight and make a slight dent in the surface film without breaking through it. Wetting is also prevented by surrounding the body with a thin layer of air. The undersides of pond skaters, for instance, are covered with a layer of closely packed microscopic knobs, like a cobbled road. The knobs trap air so that the pond skater immediately bobs up if it touches the water surface. Insects not adapted in this way for aquatic life are trapped by surface tension if they fall into the water. Their frantic struggles cannot pull them clear and only attract predatory fish and water insects.

THE PARTS OF A POND

The pond environment can be divided into four main zones whose differences emphasise the diversity of pond life. The zones are not completely exclusive – some species cross the borders – but within each the animals are adapted for very different ways of life.

The surface film is, as its name implies, a thin layer covering the whole pond. It forms the interface between the pond and the atmosphere and is the site for the exchange of life-giving gases. It is also the home of animals which make use of the properties of surface tension to rest on either upper or lower surface. The upper surface is the home of pond skaters, water crickets and springtails. Surface tension allows them to skim over the pond without sinking through it. Springtails are small, pinhead-sized insects and, when they gather in a sheltered place, they can be mistaken for a patch of bluish dust on the water surface. But stirring the water with a stick dispels the illusion; the springtails leap away in all directions. Whirligig beetles spin in small groups in sheltered places, except for the hairy whirligig which lives in running water, coming out only at night. Whirligigs float high in the water because only their undersurface is wettable; their upper parts have water repellent powers. These surface animals are generally predators and scavengers feeding on insects that have fallen onto the water.

2 A small Scottish loch formed by the damming of a valley with glacial debris. The margins are being invaded by bulrush and water-lilies

Under the surface there are animals which have come up from the depths to breathe. Waterboatmen, beetles and mosquito larvae use the surface tension to hold them at the surface, as does *Scapholeberis,* a water flea that lives upside down. It cruises about the pond, sweeping up minute algae and pollen grains trapped in the surface layer.

The open-water zone makes up the bulk of ponds that are not too overgrown. If there are no predatory fish, the open water will be colonised by water beetles, mosquito larvae and several small crustaceans, such as *Cyclops* and various species of water flea. Then there are the eight-legged water mites which suck the blood of insects, and the rotifers or wheel animals. These small animals are collectively known as plankton, from the Greek for 'that which floats'. Their swimming ability is limited and they are at the mercy of currents. Planktonic animals are not so important in ponds as they are in lakes, although they are food for minnows and sticklebacks.

When the surface-dwelling and planktonic forms of life die, their remains sink to the bottom. Along with fallen leaves, they are attacked and broken up by decomposer organisms to make mud. The bottom mud zone is inhabited by a variety of worms and insect larvae, some wandering over the surface, others burying themselves. They feed on the particles from dead organisms. Freshwater mussels lie in the mud, drawing streams of water through their body to sieve off these minute food particles.

The decomposition of animal and plant matter uses up oxygen and severe shortages can arise. Bloodworms, so-called because their bodies are red with the blood pigment haemoglobin, use this haemoglobin as a 'sponge' to take up even the tiniest amounts of oxygen, the worms coming out of their tubes and waving their bodies to increase the volume of water being 'mopped'. Consequently, they can live in water so badly polluted that little else can survive. They are joined by the rat-tailed maggot, larva of the hoverfly, which has a telescopic breathing tube that can extend 4in to penetrate the water surface like a submarine's snorkel. Those bottom-living animals that breathe by gills have to keep them clear of mud. Mayfly nymphs and the water hog louse (a relative of the woodlice) have a hairy gill cover which strains out the mud. Most of these bottom animals feed on mud or algae growing on stones, but some dragonfly larvae live here, feeding on the other insects.

The last and most important of the four zones is the plant zone which varies from a fringe around the edge to a complete choking of the pond. Here may be found the great abundance of pond animals which feed on plant tissues or seek shelter among the stems and leaves. Perhaps the most profitable method of pond-collection is to sort through the vegetation in search of the animals adhering to them.

3

BACKGROUND TO POND LIFE

How animals and plants make a living in a particular place, and the relationships of the animals and plants with one another, is called ecology. Derived from the Greek word for house *Oikos* meaning, literally, the study of the household, ecology is defined as the study of animals or plants in relation to their environment. A few years ago it was a word used only by biologists, but the new awareness of Man's relations with his own environment and the danger that he may eventually destroy it has brought the concept into popular use.

No animal or plant lives in isolation; it is part of a complex network of species which must be considered as a whole. This means that we cannot attack one species, perhaps crop it for food or harass it as a pest, and not expect there to be repercussions elsewhere. If one mesh in the network is broken, the thread runs and the net dissolves, a point made by Rachel Carson's famous book *Silent Spring.*

The work of the ecologist is to disentangle the meshes in the network of animals and plants. It is a difficult task which can be attacked in one of three ways. An ecologist may elect to study the organism itself, investigating every facet of an animal's life: breeding, feeding, distribution and so on. Or he may study relations: who eats whom, for instance. Thirdly, he may study a particular environment, its physical characteristics and how these affect the animals and plants living there. When ecology first emerged as a branch of biology it became clear that a community of plants and animals was associated with a particular place. Then it was realised that the community actually alters the place, which in turn leads to a change in the community. For instance, if reeds start to grow in open water around a pond's edge, mud and rotting vegetation accumulate among their stems. As the pond's edge has now changed, the mud attracts kingcups and water forget-me-nots that could not grow in open water.

The living community and the physical environment are, therefore, parts of a single system, called an ecosystem, which has to be considered as a whole if the lives of its inhabitants are to be appreciated. A pond is an ecosystem; so is a hedgerow, a sandy beach or an oak wood. Within the ecosystem each species has its ecological niche or its way of making a living. Part of the niche is its home or habitat, which may be so precisely defined that ecologists talk of a microhabitat. Some caddis-fly larvae are fussy about which side of a stone they live on: the stream is their habitat and the particular face of the stone is the microhabitat. The animal also has to have a profession, which is the way it gets its food. We say that some species have a broad niche because they obtain their food from many sources and live in a variety of places.

THE CHANGING POND

A pond is dynamic. Its life is continually changing. A healthy population of a particular animal may simply vanish, for no apparent reason. Other animals appear just as suddenly, stay for a short time and go, or become permanent inhabitants. The rapid changes in the pond environment make it more interesting because we can see how animals and plants adapt to them. The pond is also a microcosm, a small self-contained world where all kinds of animals live, breed and come into conflict with other species as predators, as prey or as competitors.

Ponds are often so well sheltered that no wind stirs the glassy surface. Nothing would appear to be more peaceful and stable than a pond sheltered by trees on a still, hot day, but the stillness reduces the capacity of the pond to absorb oxygen from the air. Meanwhile, under the surface plants and animals are growing and active. They are rapidly using the reserves of oxygen. The plants restore the balance by the liberation of oxygen during photosynthesis, but nightfall sees the end of this process while respiration continues unchecked. In the worst conditions, a pond may become almost devoid of oxygen towards the end of the night. Only daybreak and a new burst of photosynthesis can save the animals from suffocation.

The greatest disaster to human eyes is that the pond may dry up, but this does not mean the end of the pond community. Both plants and animals are still there ready to spring to life. Some plants will already be flourishing. Amphibious bistort, a plant with a cluster of pinkish flowers, grows equally well in land or in water and is not affected by drought. Other plants soon sprout from resting rhizomes or seeds. Many individual animals will have died in the drought, but we shall see in Chapters 4 and 5 how species survive by some individuals emigrating to other ponds, in the case of flying insects, or by the production of a resistant stage. Worms and some larvae burrow into the damp mud; snails resist drying up by sealing off the mouth of their shells; and many pond animals produce eggs with thick shells that survive the drought. Others, such as the eggs of stoneflies and mayflies, cannot survive prolonged dryness. These hatch at the appointed time no matter what conditions are like and, if there is no water, the larvae simply die. Colonisation of the newly-filled pond has to restart by immigration of adults.

Some crustaceans are better able to survive drought by the production of special drought-resistant 'resting' eggs. The water flea *Daphnia* (p 59), a common inhabitant of ponds, breeds rapidly when food is plentiful during the summer months, but overcrowding or shortage of food ensues and this is made worse by the pond drying up or by the onset of winter. The water fleas now lay resting eggs which remain inert throughout the period of drought or dearth and hatch only when conditions improve. This can be several years later. Dig up some mud from the bottom of a dry pond and place it in an aquarium. Fill with water sterilized by boiling and cover. Eventually plants and animals will appear.

As water returns to the pond, it is recolonised by the flying insects that fled the drought. The first to be seen are often pond skaters which may settle on the smallest rain puddle. Water beetles and waterboatmen (p 42) soon follow. Their return is routine as the adult insects frequently take to the air in search of a new home, so it is a simple matter of time before they find the reincarnated pond. Of greater interest is the appearance of animals that cannot travel overland themselves. A garden pond filled with filtered tap water will eventually develop its quota of crustaceans, snails, protozoans and others.

How these animals arrive can only be conjectured. The means of transport is difficult to study systematically but there are instances of animals being carried on the feathers of birds or fur of mammals, and small pea-shell cockles have been found clamped to the feet of frogs, toads and newts. This is a field that is wide open for investigation. If the thought does not appal, it is worth giving newly dead water birds a close examination. There may be small animals or seeds adhering to the plumage and feet, or even lying undigested in the crop.

THE WEB OF LIFE

The starting point in any investigation into the relationships of animals is the food chain. We have already seen that plants get their carbohydrates from photosynthesis. Animals cannot manufacture their own food so they have to depend on plants for food to fuel the body processes of movement, growth, digestion and so on. So the first link in the food chain must consist of herbivores, the plant-eating animals. They are eaten by the primary carnivores, the flesh eaters, which are preyed upon in turn by secondary carnivores and thus the energy initially trapped by the plant during photosynthesis is passed progressively along the chain. A simple example of a food chain is shown on the following page :

Sun's energy → Algae (plant) → Tadpole (herbivore) → Fish (primary carnivore) →

Kingfisher (secondary carnivore)

Because, at each stage, some energy is used up in movement and keeping the body working rather than in growth, the total weight of living matter, called the biomass, decreases at each link in the chain; so we find there are fewer carnivores, such as kingfishers, herons or pike, than there are herbivores. It may seem rather obvious, for instance, that there are more zebras than lions on the African plains, but the ratio between the size of an animal population and its food is of especial interest, particularly when considering the animal's management. There is no point in stocking a pond with trout if there is not enough for them to eat.

So far we have ignored one vital link in the food chain. The decomposing organisms, such as bacteria, form the link that closes the chain into a circle. When a plant or animal dies, bacteria set to work on its tissues. They use up energy in breaking down the tissues and returning them to the environment where they become available for the plants again. Most of the bacteria work unnoticed, breaking down the complex substances in the animal tissues to water, carbon dioxide and ammonia. Then other bacteria convert the ammonia into nitrate salts which can be absorbed by plants. These processes require oxygen and in its absence a different set of reactions takes place. The effects of bacteria working under such anaerobic conditions soon become apparent. Hydrogen sulphide (rotten egg gas) bubbles to the surface to make the pond evil-smelling. 'Iron bacteria' produce rusty deposits of ferric hydroxide while another kind makes an oily scum so that a stagnant pool looks as if it has been used as a dump for rusty machinery. Finally, certain bacteria produce marsh gas or methane which can be seen bubbling up from the bottom and sometimes is ignited by the spontaneous combustion of other products of decay. The eerie, dancing flame of burning methane was known as 'Will o' the wisp' or 'Jack o' lantern', a lamp that lured benighted travellers into swamps in the days when main roads were no more than rough tracks through an untamed countryside.

The food chain is, of course, an oversimplification because most animals eat a variety of foods and are hunted in turn by a variety of predators. The predatory stickleback, for instance, may eat insect larvae, small snails and tadpoles, and it is hunted by pike and otters as well as by ducks. A more realistic picture of the relationships in an ecosystem can be seen from a food web which is a series of interconnected food chains. The balance of a food web depends on more than the relations between an animal and its food. At each level, there will be animals competing against each other for a limited supply of food, or for living space. An extension of the idea of an ecological niche is that two species cannot share one niche. One or other gains the upper hand and forces its competitor into extinction, or nearly so. This is called the Law of Competitive Exclusion. If two species of water flea are kept in an aquarium, only one survives. It grows faster and exploits food and living space more efficiently, so it elbows out the other. The law sometimes appears to be broken by two animals giving every appearance of coexisting happily, but this is an illusion. A closer look shows that they are not competing but occupying slightly different niches. Both may prey on the same animal, but one catches larger individuals, or hunts at a different time of day.

This has been a brief summary of the pond environment but we can see the basic features that mould the lives of the animals and plants that live there. In the next section we shall be looking at the adaptations – anatomical, physiological and behavioural – of those animals and plants that lie within reach of the amateur naturalist equipped with wellingtons and net and that can be kept in aquaria. To a great extent this implies looking at and exploring ponds, but it does not exclude the fringes of lakes and running waters, particularly small streams.

4

LESSER POND ANIMALS

Several pond inhabitants – some well-known, others less familiar – have already made an appearance on these pages to illustrate features of the pond and its community. Let us now look at a wider selection of pond plants and animals more closely and enlarge upon the lives of some, either in their natural habitat or by bringing them into an aquarium. Anyone can collect the smaller animals and keep them at home, to see for himself how well they are equipped for a watery existence. As the list of animals is not exhaustive, equip yourself with a comprehensive book on freshwater animals and go on to look at others and see how they compare. These chapters are not so much a census of the pond population as an exposé of the lives of the most important and influential inhabitants.

MINUTE FORMS OF LIFE

Size prevents our watching many pond animals without a microscope but it is not necessary to use a particularly high-power instrument to reveal the lives of some minute animals and many are extremely common and easily kept. The divisions between plant and animal become blurred at this level of life. Some creatures have an animal's power of movement but a plant's capacity to produce its own food by photosynthesis. A common single-celled example is *Euglena* which corkscrews through the water by the beating of whip-like flagella. Larger, and visible to the naked eye as a green pinhead, is *Volvox*, a colony of hundreds of *Euglena*-like cells embedded in a globe of jelly, that tumbles through the water. Undeniably animal in nature are *Amoeba*, popularly regarded as the most primitive of all animals, and *Vorticella*, the 'bell-animalcule' that looks like a balloon on the end of a string anchored to the surface of a plant.

These single-celled creatures are protozoans, a word that means 'first animals', which is rather begging the question of their pedigree. Nevertheless it is a convenient term. At one time protozoans were called Infusoria because they can be cultured in an infusion of hay or other vegetable material and infusorian is a term still used for any microscopic floating freshwater organism.

Protozoans may be found almost anywhere but the best places are learned by experience. A good start can be made by running a net across the surface of a pond and scooping up a few duck-weed fronds. This will yield mainly the green, photosynthetic protozoans while amoebas can be collected by skimming across the surface of the mud with a jamjar. Let the mud settle overnight then the amoebas can be seen as minute specks on the inside of the glass. The yield in fishing for protozoans is small but their numbers can be increased by adding an 'infusion'. The standard recipe for this is to boil chopped hay in rain water and leave to stand for twenty-four hours in a narrow-necked bottle stoppered with cotton-wool. The nutrients in the hay are released by boiling and they go to feed a colony of bacteria. The infusion is added to the jar of protozoans (one part infusion to five of the original pond water) and the protozoans thrive either on the nutrients from the hay or on the bacteria.

The microscope shows something of the feeding habits of our protozoans. *Amoeba* wanders aimlessly across the microscope field, looking like a shapeless blob, although each species has a characteristic shape. It moves by pushing out temporary feet (pseudopodia) from the main body. If the *Amoeba* is floating, its pseudopodia point in all directions but, as it touches a solid surface, one takes a grip and the *Amoeba* gradually crawls forward. *Amoeba* feeds on smaller protozoans and rotifers which it engulfs. Contact with prey causes a cup-shaped depression to form at the end of a pseudopodium. This closes over the prey which is soon encased by a food bubble or vacuole into which digestive enzymes are poured so that the tiny organism is digested and absorbed.

Even the physiology of digestion can be investigated in *Paramoecium*, although it is an active swimmer, spinning through the water almost too fast to follow. Luckily, *Paramoecium* feeds only when it is stationary. It has a permanent mouth situated at the end of the oral groove which runs along the body. The cilia, which cover the body and are responsible for propelling the animal, beat strongly in this region, driving small particles along the oral groove and into the mouth.

Paramoecium feeds on bacteria and other small organisms and has the capacity to reject other particles. Food is gathered in a vacuole which separates from the bottom of the mouth and circulates around the body until it reaches an excretory vacuole permanently situated at the surface of the body. There, waste products are ejected. The process of digestion is watched by feeding *Paramoecium* with yeast cells or other fine particles stained with the indicator dye 'congo red'. When the food vacuole is first formed the congo red turns blue, indicating an acid environment, later it turns red, indicating alkaline conditions. A similar change from acid to alkaline environment also takes place as food passes along our own digestive system. Enzymes in the stomach work in acid conditions, those lower down work in alkaline solutions.

Rotifers, once known as the wheel animalcules, were formerly classed with the protozoans as 'infusoria' because of their small size and ability to grow in infusions of hay or other vegetable material. Most rotifers are about the same size as the protozoans living in the same water and the largest are only $\frac{1}{10}$in long. However, close examination shows that the two are very different for, despite their minute size, the rotifers have a complex internal anatomy that includes nervous, digestive and excretory organs. But the character by which rotifers are instantly recognised is the crown of rapidly beating cilia which looks like a tiny spinning cog-wheel and led to the choice of name from the Latin *rota* wheel, *fero* bear. The cilia perform the dual function of propelling the rotifer through the water and drawing even smaller animals and algae to the mouth that lies between the crown. As the rotifer's body is almost transparent, it does not require much skill with a microscope to watch food passing through the gut.

HYDRA

A good animal to keep in a small pond or indoor tank is *Hydra*, the freshwater relative of the sea anemones. There are three common species: the green, the brown and the slender. Hydras can be found in most ponds, usually on the underside of duckweed fronds. Place some duckweed, or a piece of waterlily leaf, in a glass bowl of water and leave it by the window (not in direct sunlight). Hydras will slowly move towards the bright side and, if the bowl is gently turned round, they can be seen hanging from the leaves or from the side of the bowl, with

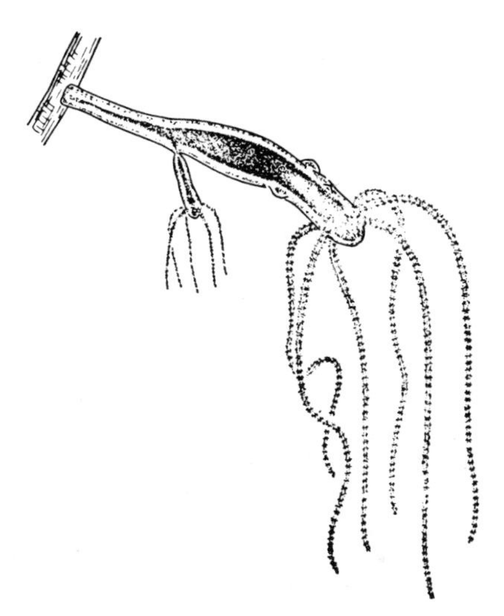

3 Freshwater *Hydra*

their tentacles trailing. Taking care not to disturb them by knocking the bowl, hydras can then be examined with a hand lens.

Hydra is basically an empty bag and at one time hydras and their relatives the sea anemones had the scientific name Coelenterata meaning 'hollow-stomached animals'. The base of the bag is anchored to a water plant and carries a ring of tentacles around the mouth. *Hydra* is carnivorous, eating water fleas, fish fry and the like which blunder into its tentacles. These are armed with stinging cells that subdue and anchor the prey like harpoons; the tentacles can thus bundle the captive animals into the mouth. Some hydras also have a built-in life-support system in the form of algae living in their tissues. Using the carbon dioxide produced by the hydra's respiration, the algae make the sugar maltose by photosynthesis. The maltose is converted into glucose by the hydra and added to the sugars it has obtained by digesting its prey. Well-fed hydra do not make much from this exchange but the maltose is a welcome 'iron ration' for a starving hydra.

Although seemingly rooted to the spot, a hydra can move. Prodding will only make it clamp down harder, but revolving its bowl 'home' will induce it to move towards the light. It travels by an imperceptible sliding along the surface rather like a snail, or by a series of cartwheels. The hydra bends over, grips the surface with its tentacles, detaching its base and somersaulting to a new place of attachment. It also swims, releasing its hold and moving through the water by vigorous writhing.

If the hydra is well-fed it will start to reproduce asexually. Round, wart-like buds develop on the side of the body and grow into new hydras. For a while 'mother' and 'daughters' live a communual life. Their 'stomachs' interconnect and food is shared. Then the 'daughters' nip off at the base and become detached to lead an independent life. As budding continues, overcrowding and a shortage of food results, so sexual reproduction starts. In natural conditions this happens in late summer when food supplies dwindle. Sex organs appear in the form of lumps, rather like the asexual buds, on the outside of the body. Ovaries grow near the base and testes near the tentacles. The ripe testes burst and liberate sperms which swim through the water in search of the ovaries where they fertilise the single egg. After fertilisation a hard coat forms over the egg and it drops off the parent, to lie dormant, surviving drought or winter. Hatching takes place and baby hydras appear when conditions become favourable again.

WORMS

As the name suggests, flatworms are flat creatures. Usually found under stones or leaves by day, they emerge at night, sliding along on a trail of slime or wriggling by muscular contractions of the body. If food, in the form of small animals, is in short supply, flatworms survive by eating themselves. They gradually shrink as they digest first their reproductive organs and then the gut and muscles. When a meal is eventually obtained, the worms regrow.

Many roundworms are parasitic but others live a free-ranging life in soil or water. They have long, slender bodies, pointed at both ends and, surprisingly, are more closely related to the rotifers than to the other kinds of worms, except for the hairworms which, from their appearance in horse troughs, led to the old folklore that they were horsehairs come to life.

Ringed worms, sometimes called the true worms, are familiar to most people as their number includes earthworms, leeches and the seaside lugworm. The body is made up of a large number of rings or segments which form separate compartments, each with its own set of internal organs and furnished with bristles, or setae, which aid movement. An earthworm has very short, virtually invisible setae but they can be heard rustling if the worm is allowed to crawl over a sheet of paper, and they are efficient anchors when a bird is trying to pull a worm out of the ground.

Freshwater relatives of the earthworm are usually only a

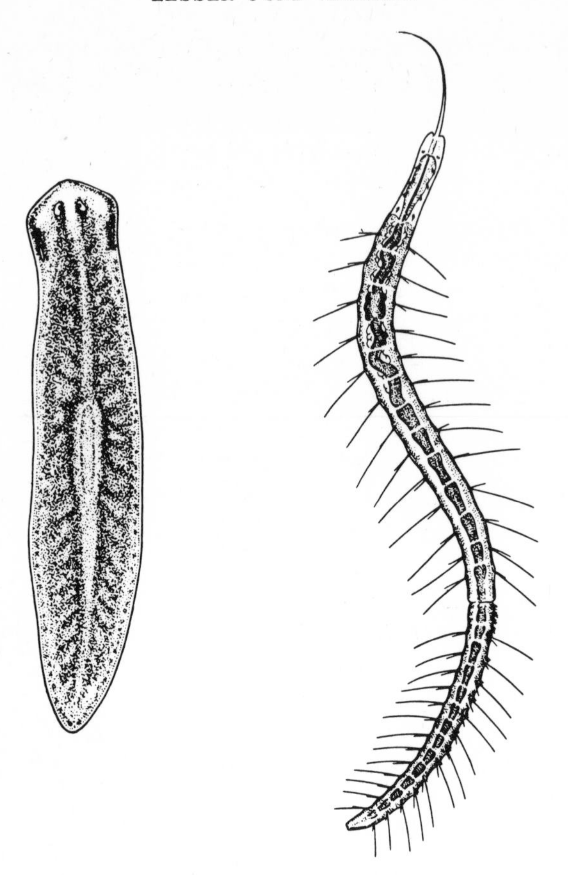

(*left*) 4 Flatworm *Dugesia lugubris*;
(*right*) 5 *Stylaria lacustris*

fraction of an inch long and live in mud or on plants. Even if the mud is sifted many of these worms are not immediately obvious because their bodies are transparent. *Stylaria*, an interesting worm that lives on the surface of water plants is recognised easily by the single tentacle protruding from the head and the rows of needle-like setae. The beauty of this worm is that its transparency enables the workings of the body organs to be examined under a low-power microscope. Sometimes a *Stylaria* worm can be seen divided into sections like the coaches of a railway train. This is the process of reproduction by budding and it is possible to watch the final separation of the sections.

Two other worms of the earthworm type are worth a mention – pot worms, which can be seen as small white worms living among the roots of water plants, and the red *Tubifex* worms. The latter are found in mud at the margins of ponds and rivers where they show up as a reddish discoloration. *Tubifex* can survive where there is the minimum of oxygen and may be the only animals in polluted waters. They live with their heads buried in the mud and their tails waving in the water.

As leeches are an almost universal object of horror it is probably a good thing that many people do not realise how common these worms are in ponds and streams. Leeches normally lead retiring lives under stones or among pondweeds but they can sometimes be seen actively moving around. Their characteristic is the suckers on head and tail, and the usual method of progression is to hold fast with the tail sucker and stretch the body out, while feeling about with the head for another suitable anchorage. When one has been found, the head sucker clamps down and the tail is brought forward. But leeches may also detach themselves completely and swim through the water with graceful undulations.

The only British leech that deserves a bad name is the medicinal leech, used for blood-letting in the days when draining blood from the body was considered such a sovereign remedy for so many ailments that doctors were even called leeches. Like many kinds of leeches, the medicinal species possesses a set of jaws that chews a hole in the victim's skin and the resulting flow of blood is maintained by an anticoagulant saliva. When the leech has had enough, it simply releases its hold and drops off. The medicinal leech is now rare in Britain probably because livestock, which were its main source of blood meals, are now generally restrained from drinking at ponds and streams in favour of troughs supplied with piped water. No other British leech can penetrate human skin, not even the large horse leech

6 Horse leech

which is not a blood sucker but swallows snails, worms and fish whole.

POND SNAILS, MUSSELS AND COCKLES

Two kinds of soft-bodied mollusc live in ponds. Those with a single shell are called gastropods, from the Greek words for stomach and foot. This group includes the pond snails and the two freshwater limpets. The second group are called bivalves, a self explanatory name as they have a shell with two parts or valves like freshwater mussels and cockles.

The two kinds of water snail are amongst the most familiar pond animals. Operculate snails have a plate or operculum which is used as a trapdoor to close the entrance of the shell, and they breathe through gills. They are usually found in running water, leaving ponds to the pulmonate snails which have lungs but no plate 'door'. Pulmonate snails include pond snails, ramshorn snails and freshwater limpets. Pond snails and ramshorns can survive in the frequently oxygen-deficient water of ponds because they obtain their oxygen from atmospheric air. Within the shell is a cavity that acts as a lung and opens to the outside world by a small tube on the snail's right-hand side. The snail comes to the surface at intervals, sometimes lying upside down with the foot pressed through the surface film, and replenishes the air in the lung by pumping movements of the body, then the breathing aperture closes and the snail submerges. If it is disturbed

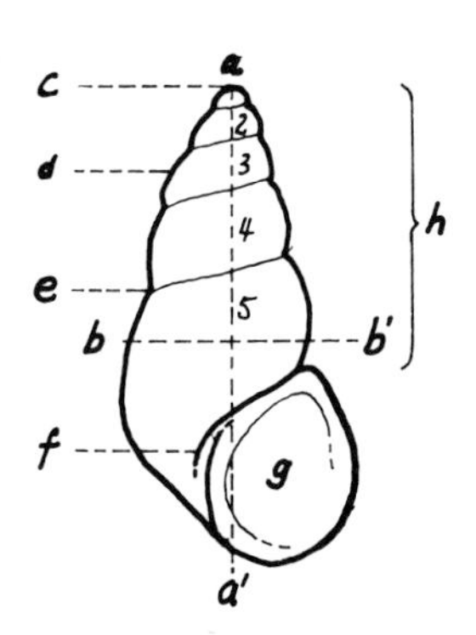

a – a' – Axis (height of shell)
b – b' – Width of shell
c – Apex
d – Single Whorl
e – Seam
f – Umbilicus
g – Aperture
h – Whorls

7 Pond snail

and needs to go down in a hurry, the snail can quickly squeeze the cavity, expel air and sink like a stone. To surface again, it enlarges the cavity to reduce the overall density of its body and bobs to the surface.

Ramshorn snails, known in America as wheel snails because the whorls of the shell are flat like a Catherine wheel, sometimes live on pond bottoms in deep water because they can turn the lung into a gill by filling it with water. Their blood also contains the red, oxygen-carrying pigment haemoglobin so that they are better able to extract oxygen from the water. In shallow water, where it is easy to come up and breathe, ramshorn snails keep the lung full of air. The haemoglobin now extracts oxygen efficiently from the air and, if ramshorns are kept in an aquarium with other pulmonates, they will be found to surface less frequently because the haemoglobin gives them an extra oxygen supply. In well-aerated water, ramshorn snails can stay submerged indefinitely.

Pond snails are often kept in home aquaria to keep down the growth of algae on the glass. It is unlikely that they will have any real chance of combatting a heavy growth, but snails are worth keeping for their own sakes. As a snail climbs along the aquarium glass, waves of muscular contraction on the underside of the foot propel it forwards and, at the same time, it scrapes at the coating of algae. Inside the snail's mouth is a tongue, the radula, furnished with rows of fine teeth like a carpenter's rasp. It tears off algae or scours the tissues from pondweeds and, when working on the side of the aquarium, leaves a zig-zag trail as the snail's head sweeps from side to side. The great pond snail, whose shell may grow to 2in long, is not content with plant food. It eats dead animals and may even attack living ones.

Courtship, like other events in the life of a snail, is slow and leisurely, but mating is rather bizarre. Male snails 'chase' female snails, climb onto their shells and fertilise them, which seems, at first sight, to be quite a straightforward affair. However, pulmonates, which include the land snails, are hermaphrodite

8 Pond snails mating. Each one can be male or female

or bisexual, each snail possessing both male and female organs so the 'male' that climbs onto another's shell can quite easily become a 'female'! If, as sometimes happens, a mating couple meets a third snail, the 'female' may then climb onto the newcomer's shell and take the male part while 'she', herself, is being fertilised. To add to the complication, the snail may fertilise some of its own eggs, no matter whether it has mated as a male or a female. Self-fertilisation greatly assists the spread of pond snails, only one snail needing to be transported to a new pond for a thriving population to build up.

Water snails lay clutches of eggs embedded in a ribbon of thick jelly, usually placing them on the leaf of a water plant or a stone but they will also lay readily on the side of an aquarium. Exceptions to this are the viviparous snails or freshwater winkles which give birth to fully formed baby snails. The development of snail eggs and the growth of the young can be best studied by lifting off the jelly ribbon with a razor blade and keeping it in a shallow dish of water. If the dish is glass or plastic, the eggs are easy to observe with a hand lens or low-power microscope, but care must be taken to see that they do not dry up.

Freshwater mussels and cockles are found only when mud or gravel brought up by dredging the pond bed is sifted. The largest of these bivalve molluscs is the swan mussel, whose shells are about 5in long. Freshwater cockles usually live in mud but some climb the stems of water plants. They are an important food for fishes and birds.

As with all bivalves, the soft fleshy body is very simple. There is no head and the main parts are the strong muscles that close the shells, the foot with which the mussel ploughs slowly through the mud, and the gills, covered with a carpet of cilia whose beating draws a current of water through the shells. If a harmless dye, such as cochineal, is added to water with an eyedropper just above the mussel, you can see water being drawn into the mussel through a short tube, the inhalant siphon, and expelled through a second, larger tube with a frilly fringe, the exhalant siphon. The stream of water serves three purposes. It provides a constant supply of oxygen to be absorbed by the gills, and it brings in minute algae and animals which are trapped by a sticky secretion on the gills and passed by the beating cilia to the mouth. This diet of minute living things might seem to make mussels a useful inhabitant of an aquarium as they filter the water clean but, unfortunately, they have a habit of dying unnoticed and fouling the water. The third use of the water flow is to draw in sperms shed into the water by male mussels. The eggs are fertilised inside the body and the larvae, which look like miniatures of the adult, are ejected through the exhalant siphon. The larvae, called glochidia, swim about clapping their shells together. They are searching for a fish to which they will cling by means of a sticky thread while digging into its skin with their sharp-edged shells. There they develop as parasites, getting nourishment from the fish's blood, until they become adult. Sticklebacks, in particular, can be found with glochidia showing as lumps on their fins and tail.

5

INSECTS AND THEIR RELATIVES

Look into a pond or sweep it with a net and the majority of creatures discovered will be the many kinds of insects or other animals whose bodies are protected by a thickened skin, like a suit of armour, and which propel themselves with an array of limbs. These are the joint-legged animals (arthropods), a huge assembly of animals that embraces insects, spiders and crustaceans. Crustaceans, in turn, include crabs and shrimps, woodlice and freshwater crayfish, water fleas and fairy shrimps. A complete list of arthropod types would be lengthy and boring to all but the keenest naturalist, as the group also includes centipedes, millipedes, scorpions and other little-known creeping animals, but the common varieties include the most interesting pond animals.

The general description that fits all arthropods is of an animal with a tough skin and, typically, the body bears a row of paired limbs, each of which is adapted for a particular function. The head carries a pair of antennae, which are usually delicate sense organs of touch and taste, although the water flea uses its stout antennae for swimming. Behind the antennae lie several pairs of mouthparts, including the jaws and others that grab, manipulate and chew food. Mosquitoes and bugs have changed their mouthparts into hypodermic needles for penetrating the tissues of plants and animals and sucking their juices. Farther down the body come the limbs used for locomotion, adapted for swimming, walking or flying.

Like all animal groups, the arthropods started life in water. Most crustaceans are still tied to an aquatic existence, the exception being the woodlouse which has moved to the land. The six-legged insects with the eight-legged spiders and mites have become complete land-dwellers, and the representatives which we find in ponds are still basically land animals. How they have changed their habits and body mechanisms to make a return to underwater life possible is one of the fascinating subjects of pond study.

When a land animal returns to the water it must continue to supply its muscles and nervous system with oxygen. There are two methods open to it, either to take air down with it from the surface like a human diver, or to extract oxygen from the water using gills like a fish. Using gills is the more efficient method and is used by nearly all the truly aquatic animals. Taking down a supply of air has the disadvantage of requiring repeated visits to the surface for replenishments. We have already seen that pond snails employ both methods of breathing, and so do the pond insects. Dragonfly and mayfly nymphs are equipped with gills but most water insects must come to the surface at intervals. A further problem of readapting to an aquatic life lies in the physical differences of air and water, as the density of water makes movement more difficult and also affects the workings of sense organs concerned with touch and vibration.

BUGS AND BEETLES

Water beetles and bugs are two kinds of insect that can be considered with some of these problems in mind. Both are common in ponds and are easy to catch and keep. Some are predators, others are vegetarian. When they are kept in aquaria, a lid is essential as they readily take to the air and some of the water beetles climb up the side of the tank or an emergent plant to spend the night out of water.

Water beetles and bugs look rather alike. They have stream-lined, boat-shaped bodies and most kinds can be immediately distinguished from their terrestrial relatives by the fringe of

9 The male great diving beetle lacks the deeply grooved wing-cases of the female but has discs on the forelegs which bear suckers for grasping the female in mating

bristles on their oar-shaped hindlegs. The superficial similarity of beetle and bug masks the distinction as the two belong to different groups of the insect class. Beetles undergo a complete metamorphosis: the adult develops from a larva or grub that is very different in appearance and the transition is made inside a pupa. The forewings of the adult are hard and form the wingcases, or elytra, which protect the delicate hindwings while at rest. Bugs have an incomplete metamorphosis: the immature stage is a nymph that looks very much like the adult but has reduced wings and undeveloped sex organs. The forewings overlap at rest instead of abutting as in the beetles'. The most important practical difference is that beetles have biting mouthparts. Bugs have tubular mouthparts like a hypodermic needle.

The statement that water beetles have biting mouthparts must, however, be qualified because some larvae suck the juices of their prey. The adult great diving beetle chews its food with powerful jaws but its 2½in larva seizes tadpoles and small fishes with sickle-shaped jaws that close like a pair of calipers. Digestive enzymes are pumped down a tube running to the tip of each jaw and the tissues of the prey are turned into a predigested soup which is sucked back into the mouth. Even human fingers are not immune. The adult beetle has a second line of defence : as well as attempting to bite, it secretes an evil-smelling white fluid from the thorax. Diving beetle larvae can be seen paddling through the water in search of prey, but their rivals in ferocity, the nymphs of dragonflies, prefer to lurk in the weeds. When suitable food swims past, the nymph shoots out a clawed 'mask' to impale the victim and bring it back to the mouth.

Water bugs provide an illustration of the importance of using scientific, Latin-based names to avoid the confusion of common names. There are two kinds of bug called waterboatman : the small, round-bodied plant-eater of the family Corixidae, also called the lesser waterboatman, and the carnivorous waterboatman of the family Notonectidae. The latter most deserves the common name as it looks very much like a miniature rowboat propelled with oars. However, as it swims upside down it is becoming usual to call it a backswimmer.

Backswimmers pierce and suck the juices of their victims – other insects, tadpoles, even fishes – and may pierce the skin of a hand groping in the water, giving a nasty 'nip'. These bugs orientate by means of light. In normal circumstances sunlight comes from above, but if an aquarium is illuminated from below, the backswimmers will turn over and swim the 'right way up'. The plant-eating corixid waterboatmen dabble along the bottom, among pond weeds, stirring up then sorting out edible detritus and single-celled algae which are collected and swallowed. Larger algae are pierced with the tubular mouthparts and sucked dry.

10 The 'water tiger', larva of the great diving beetle, showing its caliper-like jaws

The hunting behaviour of the backswimmer depends on a set series of programmed behaviour. Drop an insect on the water, and the backswimmer rushes across, seizes it and sucks it dry. Yet, before it starts to feed, it has made four separate enquiries as to the edibility of the insect with each enquiry resulting in a 'go, no-go' decision like those made familiar by the American moon landings. If information received does not give the right answer, feeding behaviour does not proceed. The enquiries as to edibility are made by four sets of senses. First, the backswimmer is attracted by vibrations in the water. This can be demonstrated by rapidly vibrating a wire held with its tip in the water. The backswimmer turns to face the source of vibration then swims rapidly towards it. It can orientate towards a source up to 8in away. When only 2in away the backswimmer switches to visual orientation; it must be able to see its prey. If a thin wire is vibrated near the side of the aquarium, the backswimmer will approach then divert towards a small object, say a blob of Plasticine on a wire, held behind the aquarium glass. The vibrations are now ignored and the backswimmer attempts to seize the object. If dropped in the water, the object is seized but immediately released because the next stage in prey identification is to test the texture. Only soft objects are held. Finally, feeding is triggered by taste; the backswimmer can be persuaded to plunge its tubular mouthparts into a piece of cotton-wool impregnated with meat extract.

Waterboatmen and diving beetles breathe by air bubbles trapped on their bodies, so they are buoyant and rise to the surface as soon as they stop swimming. In fact, if weights are attached to a diving beetle, it compensates by increasing the size of its air bubble to promote buoyancy. The position of the air bubble is variable. The haplid water beetles trap air under plate-like expansions at the bases of the hindlegs, and the hydrophilid beetles carry air on the underside of the thorax and abdomen so that they float upside down. Diving beetles trap air under the wingcases. At intervals, the beetle floats to the surface, the tip of its abdomen breaking the surface of the water

11 Backswimmer poised on the underside of the surface film. The breathing tubes on the tip of the abdomen are in contact with the air

and the wingcases raised so that it looks as if some strange animal is opening a rather fearsome mouth. The two rear spiracles or breathing pores take air into the respiratory system and air is also trapped under the wingcases.

The air bubble is trapped in a dense, velvety pile of hairs which, by connecting with the animal's spiracles, acts as a gill. Oxygen dissolves from the water into the bubble and carbon dioxide dissolves out. The efficiency of the 'gill' depends on the surface area of the bubble, maintained by the large amount of nitrogen in air. Nitrogen plays no part in the chemistry of animal life but it is important to these aquatic insects as it is exchanged between air and water much more slowly than is oxygen. Thus oxygen will tend to pass from water into the bubble faster than nitrogen passes out and the shrinkage of the bubble is slow. The exchange of gases is sometimes speeded by the insect stirring the bubble with its legs and backswimmers extract oxygen equivalent to the amount in a volume of air thirteen times as large as that of the bubble without having to surface. Visits to the surface to replenish the bubble are still necessary at long intervals, but diving beetles can survive on the bottom throughout the winter by remaining inactive and taking advantage of the high oxygen-content of cold water.

The surface of a pond or slow stream is the home of whirligig beetles. These small, oval beetles spin around in groups, describing tight circles like dodgem cars. The middle and rear pairs of legs are used for swimming. They bear broad plates that fan open on the power stroke and fold to reduce drag on the recovery stroke. Their gyrations become frantic when disturbed and if a net is plunged at them they abruptly dive to the bottom. Like diving beetles, whirligigs defend themselves by exuding a fluid when molested. One American whirligig is said to smell like apples.

Whirligigs are capable of a fair turn of speed. An American whirligig has been timed at 0.9mph with bursts of 2.2mph. This does not sound very fast, but a whirligig is less than $\frac{1}{2}$in long and the fastest recorded house spiders, which seem to scuttle so fast over the floor, clock only half this speed. In general, animals can run faster than they can swim because air offers less resistance than water. So how do whirligigs achieve such speed? A whirligig lies in the water like a boat and, like a boat, its speed is fixed by the length of its body. The movement of a boat's hull sets up two series of waves, one at the bow and the other at the stern. At slow speeds the boat spans several bow waves but, as the speed increases, the wavelength (the distance between successive wave crests) increases until the second bow wave meets and reinforces the stern wave. The boat is now lying in a trough between the first bow wave and the reinforced wave at the stern. To get out of the trough and go faster needs either a prodigious expenditure of power or raising the hull out of the water by hydroplaning. The whirligig avoids this problem by its short body length. Although it does not plane, but ploughs solidly through the water, it is so short that the bow waves always have a wavelength longer than the body length so that they cannot reinforce the stern wave.

Whirligigs have to avoid their fellows during their giddy spinning. They must also keep in the middle of the pool and find their prey, which is mainly insects trapped and struggling on the water surface. Navigation is based on eyesight and sensitivity to vibration. Whirligig eyes are divided into two sections, one for looking upward the other for looking down, and the anatomical structure differs slightly so that the one is adapted for vision in air and the other for vision under water. The antennae rest lightly on the surface of the water and detect ripples made by other whirligigs and by the struggles of hapless insects that have fallen on the water and are fighting to get clear.

Whirligigs are joined at the water surface by the bugs known variously as pond skaters and water crickets. The former are very common on still waters while the latter are found on pools and backwaters of streams. Lurking among the plants but coming into the open is the water measurer or water gnat, an incredibly slender animal that paces deliberately across the pond as if measuring its width. As described in Chapter 2, such insects are supported on the water surface by the forces of surface tension. Pond skaters identify their prey in the same way as the backswimmer. The range over which vibrations in the water can be detected and the distance for switching to visual guidance are roughly the same for both animals. Once the prey has been seized, the pond skater probes and tries to pierce it. Hard objects are quickly abandoned, but soft objects are given a longer examination and feeding takes place if the sense of taste confirms edibility.

THE BITING FLIES

A variety of insects are called flies in popular language but, to the zoologist, the true flies are those with only one pair of wings. The rear pair has been converted into short, knobbed stalks, called halteres and visible under a magnifying glass. The halteres act as a kind of gyroscope to help control the insect's flight. The true flies include house flies, crane flies (daddy long legs) and horse flies, as well as the many kinds of mosquito and midge. As a group, they give us an immense amount of trouble as painful biters and carriers of disease. A fair number breed in fresh waters, or at least in damp earth surrounding ponds and rivers. The most familiar of these are the blood-sucking mosquitoes, gnats and midges. The three names are used indiscriminately in everyday English and one must resort to their scientific names to sort out the different kinds. Most of these flies would be completely overlooked if it were not for their habit of stealing a blood meal and leaving behind a painful lump, but their numbers gives them an important place in the freshwater food web.

Mosquitoes and gnats, the names are interchangeable, belong to the family Culicidae. This includes those mosquitoes which carry such fatal diseases as malaria and yellow fever. Only the females bite; they need a blood meal before their eggs can develop. The harmless male is distinguished by the feathery antennae which are a kind of ear for recognising the wing-

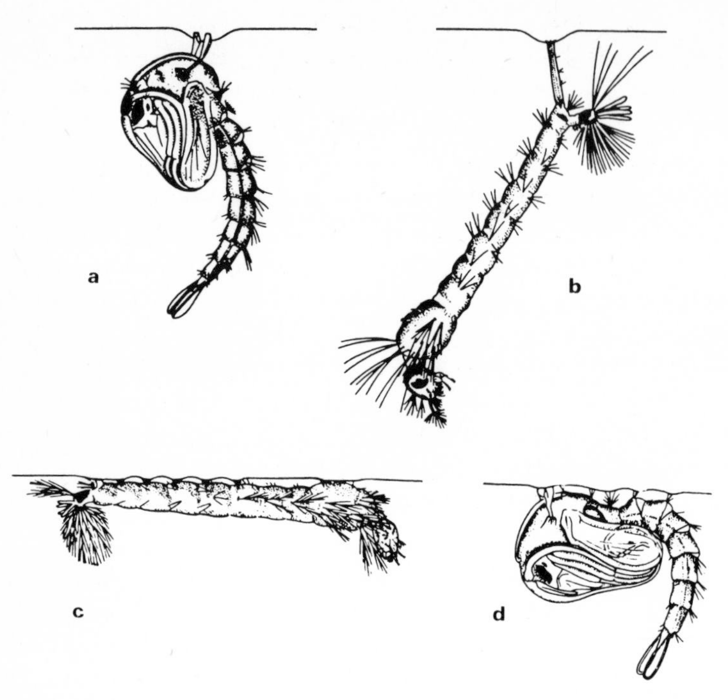

12 Mosquitoes: (a) Pupa of *Culex*; (b) Larva of *Culex*; (c) Larva of *Anopheles*; (d) Pupa of *Anopheles*

beat vibrations of the female when she is ready to mate. Larvae of one species or another can be found in most bodies of water, even in the minute pools that collect in rotten tree stumps. The eggs, laid singly in the case of *Anopheles* mosquitoes and in rafts in *Culex* mosquitoes, can be collected by skimming a small pond or bird bath. *Anopheles* are the carriers of disease and can be recognised, when adult, by the body being held parallel while at rest. *Culex* rests with the body angled to the surface. The malarial mosquito *Anopheles maculipennis* lives in Britain and malaria, or ague as it used to be called, was common in country districts until the early years of this century.

The phantom midge is another member of the Culicidae. It gets its name from the transparent larva which floats in the open water of ponds and lakes. The larvae are extremely difficult to see while they float horizontally in the water but their presence is given away by the two pairs of dark, air-filled bladders that act as buoyancy tanks. By altering the amount of air in the bladders, the larva can change its depth. Phantom larvae are carnivorous and they use their specially modified antennae to catch small animals.

Although the culicid mosquitoes are sometimes called midges, the name is better reserved for two families of small flies. The Chironomidae are extremely abundant with clouds of males gathering on fine summer evenings over water or land. Luckily they do not bite and their importance lies in the huge amount of food that they provide for other animals, either as adults or larvae. Some of the larvae, known as bloodworms, are easily mistaken for true worms (p 33). Bloodworms live in shelters of silk covered with silt, but they sometimes emerge and wriggle through the water. They get their red colouring from the pigment haemoglobin and the like *Tubifex* worms (p 35) can live in water that is very deficient in oxygen.

The biting midges belong to the family Ceratopogonidae. Called punkies or no-see-ums in North America on account of their diminutive size, their number includes the infamous Highland midge that plagues northern Scotland in summer. Holidays in the Scottish Highlands can be spoiled because outdoor activities are severely limited by either rain or midges, sometimes both, and no answer has yet been found for controlling midges. Insect repellents are not wholly effective and the occupation by the larvae of every small pool and puddle, as well as damp earth, throughout the Highland wilderness makes any programme of eradication quite impracticable.

DRAGONFLIES

Dragonflies can be watched, through binoculars, retiring to a perch to dismember their prey, to clean their vitally sensitive eyes and antennae with their forelegs, or merely basking in the sun.

13 Southern *Aeschna* dragonfly resting on the husk of the nymph from which it has just emerged. Note the huge eyes which are used in hunting

While they are resting, the differences between dragonfly and damselfly can be made out, as dragonflies rest with wings outstretched and the two pairs of wings are dissimilar. In contrast, the damselflies carry their similarly shaped pairs of wings over their backs. The older males which have weathered many fights will have tatty wings. The male dragonfly establishes a territory from which he aggressively excludes other males, although all females are welcomed and mating attempted, sometimes after a courtship display.

An insect's genitalia lie near the tip of the abdomen and mating is achieved by a single coupling. Dragonflies have an elaborate coupling mechanism which seems unnecessarily complicated and requires acrobatic mating. Before seizing the female, the male curls his abdomen forward and transfers his sperm to accessory genitalia on the thorax. Then he clasps the female's head with his legs and again curls his abdomen, but this time to seize her head with a pair of pincer-like claspers at the tip before releasing the hold of his legs. All this takes place in the air and the two dragonflies are now flying 'in tandem', coupled together with the male above and in front of the female. Insemination requires further contortions. It is now the turn of the female to curl her abdomen forward, swinging her whole body upside down so that her genitalia make contact with the male's accessory genitalia. This takes place in flight, or perched, and is a most odd-looking performance.

The pair remain coupled while the female prospects for an egg-laying site, the attachment of the male preventing any further mating which would threaten his chances of fertilising her eggs. Some dragonflies merely lay their eggs in the water, shedding them from above the surface or dipping down to brush the abdomen through the water. Dragonflies of the Aeschnidae family and the damselflies land and drill a hole in the stems or leaves of water plants. They insert their eggs into the tissues, either above or below water level and some damselflies crawl down the stem until the female and perhaps her mate are completely submerged. Their delicate wings are protected

14 A damselfly nymph showing the developing wings and the three delicate caudal gills which are used for respiration and steering

by a bubble of air which lifts the insect to the surface when egg-laying is completed.

Dragonfly nymphs are described in the next section, on mayflies and caddis flies.

MAYFLIES AND CADDIS FLIES

Mayflies get their name from the mass emergence of adult insects in late May. They are unique among insects for their extra moult. The insect that crawls out of the old nymph skin is not a full adult, but a subadult with dull colouring – the 'dun' of the angler – and the full adult is formed only after another moult. As soon as mayflies become airborne their days are numbered. The females are ready to mate almost immediately and once their eggs are laid there is nothing left to live for, so mayflies disappear again from the pond scene. The species continues as nymphs living on pond or stream bed and feeding on algae and other plants.

Mayfly nymphs bear two rows of gills on the body, marking a stage in evolution from a terrestrial way of life to a wholly aquatic existence. The operculate snails have taken this step but no insect species has completely abandoned air-breathing in the adult stage. The nearest to come to this state is the moth *Acentropus niveus* in which some of the females have minute wings. These females spend their adult lives underwater but must still come to the surface to pair and the males and fully winged females lead an aerial existence. Insect larvae have, however, become fully aquatic. Dragonfly nymphs bear gills inside the gut. Water is taken in through the anus and, if the nymph is in a hurry to escape, it can squirt the water out to propel itself forwards. Oxygenation of the blood is stimulated by the rhythmic beating of the gills which pulls a stream of fresh water over them.

The moment of emergence from the pupa is a crucial period for any insect, but is particularly so if it has to change from an aquatic to an aerial existence, and from water- to air-breathing.

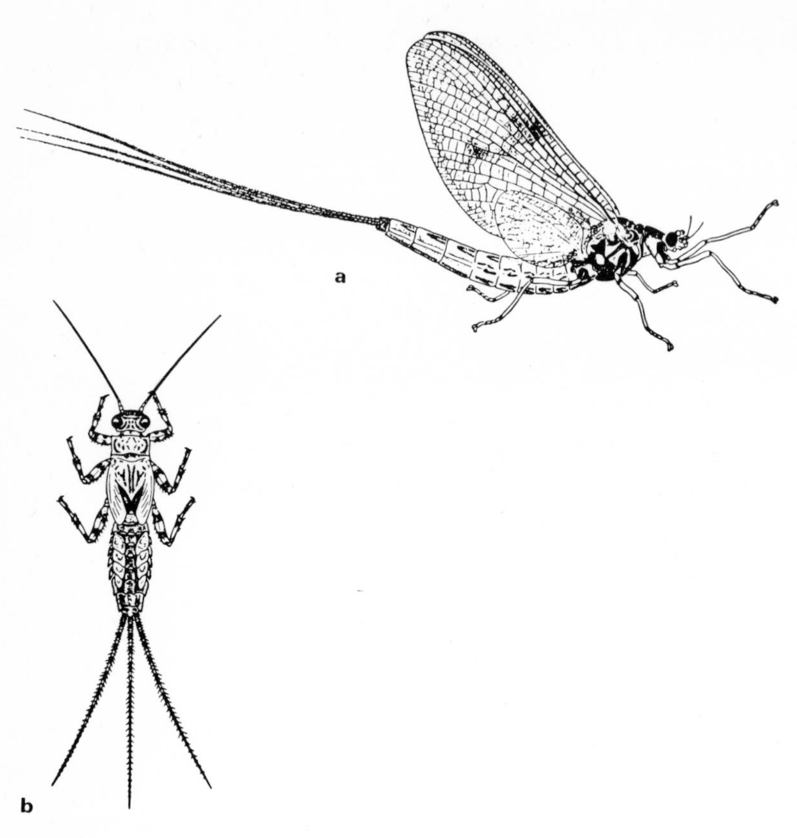

15 Mayflies: (a) Adult *Ephemera vulgata*; (b) Nymph *Ephemerella*

Dragonfly nymphs make a leisurely transformation. The nymph climbs the stem of a water plant until it is clear of the water, its skin splits open and the adult pulls itself out, then rests while the body hardens and the wings expand. Mayfly nymphs gather air between their outer skin and the skin of the winged insect that has developed inside. As a result they float to the surface where the nymphal skin splits open and the winged mayfly climbs out. Mosquitoes employ a similar trick to escape from the pupa but the black flies, true flies of the Simuliidae family, which spend their early lives attached to the bottom of the fast-running streams, must emerge in a hurry to avoid being swept away. The pupa fills with air and splits open while still in its cocoon at the bottom of the stream. The adult climbs out, bobs to the surface in a bubble of air and shoots straight into the air as its wings are already expanded and functional.

An adult caddis fly is easily mistaken for a moth and is likely to be found among moths at a lighted window after dusk. Only the microscope reveals a basic difference. Moths' wings are covered with minute scales, like roof tiles, that come off as a powder if they are rubbed. Hence, moths and butterflies are assigned to the order Lepidoptera or scale-wings. Caddis-fly wings, however, are covered with a pile of fine hairs and they are classed as Trichoptera or hair-wings. Like mayflies, caddis flies have only a brief adult life and their nymphs are much more rewarding subjects for study.

Caddis nymphs can be collected from most freshwater habitats except fine mud and polluted water, and are readily scooped up in a net or, with aid of a viewing box, seen crawling over the bottom. About 150 British caddis flies build portable cases of plant or stones but very few have had their construction habits subjected to close study. Case-building behaviour can be watched by pushing the larva out of its case by inserting the *head* end of a pin up the rear entrance. Unfortunately, the case which the larva then re-assembles around its naked body is often abnormal, but at least the mechanism of selecting and fitting new material can be seen. There is no real substitute for watching the complete larval cycle, a long-term project as eggs are laid mainly in late summer and the larvae pupate in the following spring. One advantage is that there is not much else to do in the pond-watching line at this season!

For observations of housebuilding to have any validity, it is essential to know the species of caddis fly involved. Identification of older larvae can be made with a key, as in N. H. Hickin's *Caddis Larvae,* but it is better to catch adult females which can be more readily identified and start the experiment with eggs. Adult caddis flies can be attracted and trapped by a powerful light at night. Ripe females usually have their egg masses partly extruded from the tip of the abdomen and they can be coaxed to lay on damp blotting paper. When the larvae hatch out, give each its own dish of water with a selection of building materials : sand, pebbles, twigs and leaves.

At intervals, inspect the larvae for progress. Measure the length and diameters, at head and tail end, of the cases and note the types of building material. Some species change the material used at some point and material may be shaped and orientated to make a very neat construction. Growth of the case is not regular. At intervals growth rate spurts; this happens just after each of the five moults. Sometimes, the case suddenly becomes shorter because the larva has turned around and ripped off the now redundant rear end.

WATER FLEAS AND OTHER CRUSTACEANS

Any sample of pond water is likely to have a number of small round animals bouncing up and down like miniature yo-yos. These are water fleas; not relatives of the jumping, biting insect

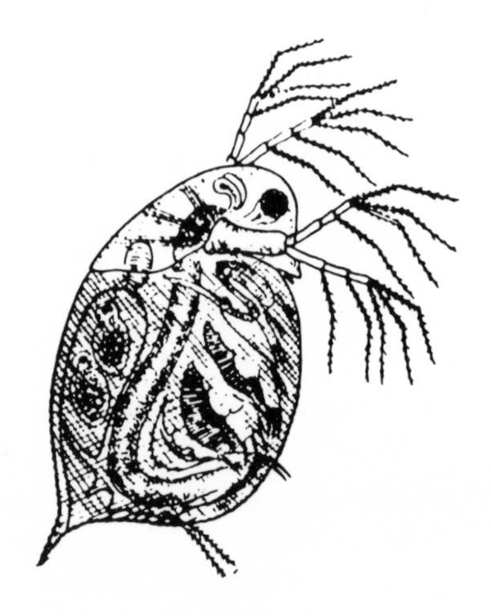

16 *Daphnia*

but crustaceans often known by their scientific name of *Daphnia*. The largest species is only $\frac{1}{5}$in long but water fleas often show up well by the sheer numbers of dancing dots in the water. Distant relatives of the crabs and lobsters, their bodies are enclosed in a carapace like the two valves of a mussel (p 40). The head bears a single eye and two pairs of antennae, one small and inconspicuous and the other large and used in swimming. Five more pairs of limbs beat constantly within the confines of the carapace to pull on a current of water. The limbs bear bristles which filter out bacteria and protozoa and pass them to the mouth.

The dancing helps to keep *Daphnia* where food is most abundant. Whereas a backswimmer that feeds on large animals tracks down each victim singly, *Daphnia* merely search for a dense concentration of floating algae. How it does this can be demonstrated quite neatly in an aquarium. If the water fleas are illuminated with red light they dance vertically but under blue light they tend to swim horizontally. The explanation is that a dense patch of green algae absorbs blue light from sunlight thereby imparting a reddish tinge. The water fleas swim about aimlessly until, by chance, they encounter reddish light whereupon they start to dance vertically. This keeps them automatically where food is plentiful.

Water fleas show two of the specialities which we have already met in pond animals. Like the *Tubifex* worms (p 35) and the bloodworms (p 51), water fleas use haemoglobin to

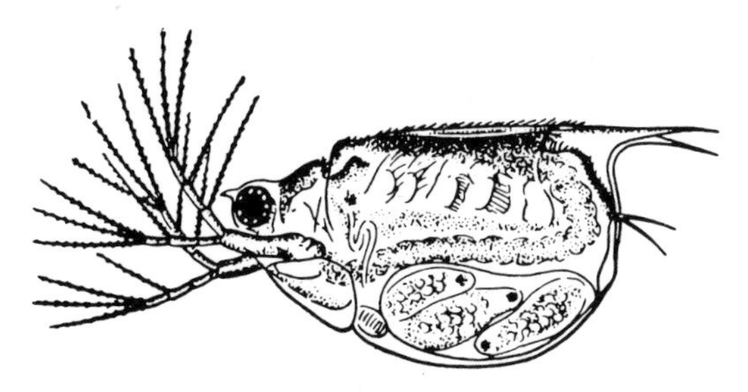

17 Water flea *Scapholeberis mucronata*

extract oxygen from poorly aerated water. Indeed, as the amount of oxygen in the water decreases, water fleas manufacture more haemoglobin and become visibly redder. We have seen how some animals react to the changing conditions of a pond by altering their mode of reproduction: rotifers and *Hydra*, for example, reproduce rapidly when conditions are favourable then produce resting stages to tide them over times of hardship. Similarly, during the summer months, only female water fleas are to be found. They breed rapidly by virgin birth and almost any water flea examined will be carrying about twenty summer eggs in a brood pouch under the carapace. Then, when food runs short or at the approach of winter, male water fleas appear. They are smaller than the females which they fertilise to produce 'winter' eggs. A brood will consist of only one or two winter eggs which are thick-shelled and are kept in the brood pouch until the water flea moults its carapace or dies. When the pond once more becomes suitable for water-

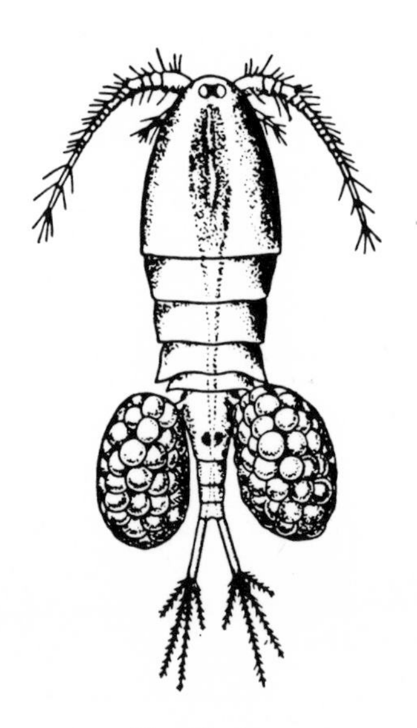

18 *Cyclops*

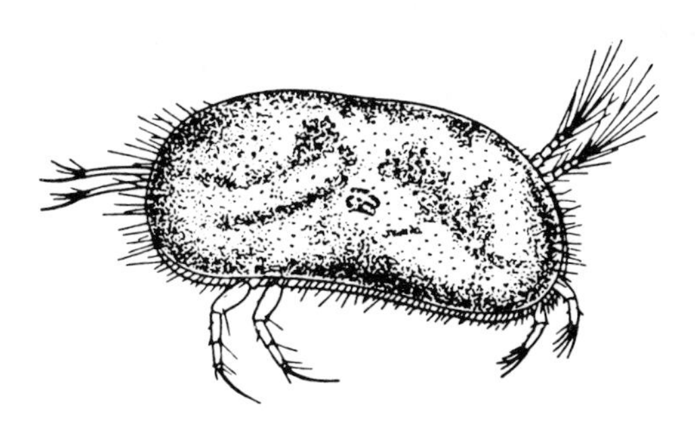

19 Ostracod *Herpetocypris reptans*

flea life, the winter eggs hatch and virgin birth rapidly restores the population.

Daphnia is only one of many kinds of crustacean living in pond water and, as with the many flies, they are very important as the food of other animals. Among the commonest crustaceans are *Cyclops,* aptly named after the one-eyed giant of Greek mythology. *Cyclops* is as small as *Daphnia* but can be identified without looking for its single eye under a microscope because of the skittle-shaped body and the one or two berry-like clusters of eggs carried at the rear. There are also the water slater or hog louse *Asellus*, which looks like and is related to the woodlouse, and the ostracods, a group of crustaceans that look like tiny beans tumbling through the water. Their bodies are enclosed in a carapace into which they can retreat when alarmed. Larger than any of these and measuring up to 1in long, is the freshwater shrimp, *Gammarus,* although this is not a very good name as it is not closely related to the seashore shrimps. Its body is flattened from side to side and is curved when at rest. Sometimes the males are found carrying the smaller female underneath their bodies.

MITES AND SPIDERS

Mites and spiders belong to the group of animals called Arachnida (from the Greek for spider). That these animals are not insects is adequately shown by the division of the body into less than three sections, the four rather than three pairs of legs and by the absence of antennae. Unlike the insects, few arachnids have taken up an aquatic existence. Although quite common, water mites are not particularly noteworthy. Their bodies are not divided into distinct parts and they look like animated buns clambering over water plants or swimming through the water.

A few spiders venture onto water, using the surface film as a kind of web. Vibrations caused by an insect becoming trapped on the surface are detected by the spider, as it would receive vibrations passing along the threads of a web, and it scuttles over the water like a pond skater to seize its victims. When disturbed, the spiders find refuge underwater, taking down a bubble of air on their bodies for breathing purposes.

The true water spider has ingeniously solved the problem of underwater life by constructing a 'diving bell' of silk. The bell is filled with air which the spider brings down from the surface as a silvery bubble trapped among the hairs of its body, and which it wipes off into the bell by stroking with its legs. The air bubble in the bell acts as a gill absorbing oxygen from the surrounding water and releasing carbon dioxide so that the spider can stay submerged for a long time. In fact, the water spider can be very boring to watch as it spends long periods curled up in its bell.

20 Water mite *Hydrodroma*

21 Water spider entering its silken, air-filled 'bell'. Note the film of air on the abdomen

When it does emerge, the spider runs over the vegetation or swims with a clumsy 8-legged dogpaddle. Its prey is small animals, such as freshwater shrimps and insect larvae, and it will also eat houseflies trapped on the water surface. Water spiders are rather unusual in that the male is larger than the female and the pair will co-exist together quite peacefully. In most spiders the male is diminutive and has to approach the female with care if he wants to mate without being eaten. But if a pair of water spiders is starved, it is the female that disappears. The main problem in trying to keep a water spider is that it can squeeze through minute crevices, so if you do have one in the home its tank must be kept securely closed with a cloth or gauze tied around the top.

6

FISHES

Unless they have been specially stocked for angling, stretches of water about the size of a village pond are not usually well-endowed with fishes except for sticklebacks, minnows and eels. Rivers, lakes and larger ponds contain a wider variety, such as gudgeon, rudd, perch, pike, roach, tench and trout, well known to the angler but not usually caught by the naturalist with his net. Some are of particular interest and fish make a very useful addition to an aquarium or garden pond. As fish tend to keep moving and many frequent the midwater level they add movement and life to the garden pond and home aquarium, so compensating for the retiring or sluggish natures of many of the invertebrate animals.

STICKLEBACKS

The most interesting of freshwater fishes must be the 3-spined stickleback, the humble 'tiddler' caught by generations of small boys, that has also taken its place as a 'textbook animal'. The 3-spined stickleback of Europe and North America is easily recognised by the three spines on its back, thus distinguishing it from the 4-spined stickleback of North America, the rarer 9-spined stickleback and the 15-spined stickleback which lives around European coasts. Despite these formidable spines, sticklebacks fall prey to many predators, such as pike, grebes, kingfishers and otters. They, themselves, feed on small crustaceans, worms, snails and the like.

As the breeding season approaches, the male 3-spined stickleback becomes brightly coloured, with red on his underside, a blue eye and greenish back. He now stakes out a territory on the bottom of pond or stream and, in weed-free, clear water he can be seen floating head-down in display. Courtship and breeding can be watched if he is caught and transferred to an indoor home.

Unless very large, an aquarium can only accommodate one breeding male because male sticklebacks are fierce in defence of their territories. The males will fight any intruding fish but are most aggressive towards other male sticklebacks. If two males are introduced to a sufficiently large aquarium both will be able to stake out territories. If they are then captured and each is imprisoned in a glass tube, when the tubes are placed in one territory, the owner of that territory will attempt to attack the other, who will try to escape. When they are moved to the other territory, the roles are reversed. So a stickleback is aggressive only when in its own territory and is timid when caught trespassing. Normally, however, it does not trespass into strange territories once the boundaries have been decided.

The stimulus that rouses the territorial sticklebacks' aggression is the red belly of the opposition which gives a simple but quite definite signal. As a practical demonstration, a male stickleback will attack a crude model fish painted red on the underside, particularly if it is held vertically to mimic the stickleback's aggressive display. The model can be so crude as to be hardly fish-like, but a perfect model or a freshly killed stickleback receives no reaction provided that there is no trace of red. Niko Tinbergen relates how the male sticklebacks in his laboratory displayed vigorously when a red mail van passed the window.

When the stickleback is secured in his territory, nest-building starts. He digs a shallow pit by removing mouthfuls of sand and fills it with a mass of algae which he binds with a sticky secretion from his kidneys. Then he drives a tunnel through the middle by wriggling into it. The nest is now complete and the stickleback is ready to mate.

22 Three-spined stickleback with its fins and spines raised. Despite the spines, sticklebacks fall prey to many animals

If anything, the male stickleback becomes even more brilliant now. The red of his belly and throat becomes more intense and the black pigment in the skin of his back contracts into dots so that he is now bluish-white with black freckles. Small parties of females swim through the territories. They are distinguished by a silvery sheen and a belly swollen with eggs. When ready for courtship, the male comes out to greet the female shoal with an effusive dance. In a series of zig-zags, he leaps first away from them, then towards them, braking to an abrupt halt. Non-receptive females turn and flee but ripe females hold their ground. The male now rushes back to the nest, with the female following, and he shows her the entrance by wriggling and turning on his side. Taking the hint, the female follows him in, but the male then slips out again and starts to butt her on the flank with his snout, trembling at the same time, which stimulates the female to shed her eggs. When finished, she slides out of the nest so that the male can enter and fertilise the eggs.

The female's role in continuing the stickleback species is now complete and the male, who had courted her so keenly, chases her away. Caring for the family is his task alone. He starts by making repairs to the nest, which may have been ripped during egg-laying, and tidies up the eggs so that they are well hidden. More females may be courted and several clutches of eggs gathered in the nest but, from the start, the male looks after his brood. Intruders are chased away and an increasing amount of time is spent in fanning the eggs which need a stream of water passing through the nest to provide oxygen for their respiration. The stream is created by the male floating head down in front of the nest entrance and beating his pectoral fins to force water through the nest. The 4-spined stickleback sucks water through the nest with his mouth.

Incubation lasts five to twelve days, depending on water temperature, and the baby sticklebacks stay in the nest for another day or so. Their father stops the fanning which has been taking up three-quarters of his time but he now has the full-time job of guarding the shoal of tiny sticklebacks for about two weeks. If any youngster strays, the male rushes after it, takes it in his mouth and spits it back into the shoal. However, each baby stickleback must evade its father once and make a mad dash to the surface. It has to take a gulp of air to inflate its swimbladder. Unless it does this it will have buoyancy problems. As the baby sticklebacks grow up, their father's interest wanes. He loses his brilliant colours and goes off to form a shoal with his contemporaries, while the babies keep in their own shoal.

MINNOWS AND CARP

Minnows are quite easy to keep at home but they must be handled carefully and transferred very quickly from net to jar or bucket. They do best when several are kept together and can swim in a shoal. As the water warms up in spring, minnows move into shallow water where they can be seen swimming in shoals over the sandy bottom. The males become brightly coloured, rather like the sticklebacks. The top part of the body darkens while the belly and the paired fins turn red. They also

23 Minnows in an aquarium swim in a shoal

grow white lumps on the head, called pearl organs. The courtship of minnows has none of the drama exhibited by sticklebacks, the female simply depositing her eggs and the baby minnows lurking among the pebbles until the yolk sac is absorbed.

Minnows feed on crustaceans, insects and worms, and even eat trout eggs. The minnows themselves are eaten by larger fish such as perch and pike, but they are not so vulnerable as living in shoals would seem to make them, as predators get confused when confronted by a massed quarry, finding it difficult to pick out one individual to chase. The one that eventually falls victim is usually a weak fish, perhaps sick or injured, that falls behind the others. As soon as one minnow is caught, the rest abandon it to its fate and flee. Their flight is triggered by an 'alarm substance', a chemical released from the captured minnow when its skin is broken. If small pieces of skin from a freshly dead minnow are dropped into an aquarium, the minnows rush about and remain panicky for some time.

Minnows are members of the carp family and their relative, the common carp, was introduced into Britain by medieval monks for their stewponds. Many other common fishes belong to the carp family, including the familiar tench, gudgeon, chub, roach and dace of the coarse angler. The gudgeon is quite a useful aquarium fish as it cleans up debris on the bottom, and the tench does well in ponds.

The European pond loach, akin to the carp, survives in muddy, weed-infested ponds by coming to the surface and gulping air which passes through the intestine where oxygen is absorbed. When the pond dries up the loach can survive by burying itself in the mud. The pond loach and the stone loach, which occurs in Britain, are together called weather-fish. Both, but particularly the pond loach, are sensitive to a rise in barometric pressure, such as occurs before a thunderstorm. The fish become agitated and constantly swim to the surface, their behaviour being such a clear manifestation of an imminent change in weather that they used to be kept as weather forecasters.

EELS

Eels are mainly nocturnal and hide up under cover during the day so that they are not the most exciting animals to watch in an aquarium. However, they can survive in stagnant water and even travel overland to reach isolated ponds. Like amphibians, eels breathe to a large extent through the skin, as much as 60 per cent of their oxygen being obtained in this manner. Female eels in particular are great travellers and on dark nights can be found on dry land, travelling to isolated lakes and ponds.

Eels can also be seen climbing the walls of dams and sluices. Their slender bodies and powerful muscles enable them to make use of every irregularity to maintain a hold.

PERCH AND PIKE

The two predators in the world of freshwater fishes are perch and pike. Both hunt by ambush, lying in wait and catching their prey by a sudden pounce rather than by a long chase in open water. Pike are the original 'fish that got away' and are the basis for many a fishy story about size, age and ferocity. Yet they well deserve the name of freshwater shark, with the long body and shovel-shaped mouth which contains sharp teeth on the roof of the mouth as well as in the jaws. Pike spend most of their time in inactivity. They lurk in the weeds camouflaged by a mottled green skin until suitable prey swims past when they move slowly forwards and spring out in a tremendous burst of speed. The final dash may take the pike 30ft in a straight line and it is guided by stereoscopic vision, the long snout having two 'sighting grooves' which allow clear forward vision. The main prey is fishes including smaller pike, but water voles, moorhens and ducks are also captured, so that pike are not a welcome addition to the pond unless the larger specimens are caught and removed.

Perch live in lakes and rivers but also in the larger ponds providing there is a reasonable amount of oxygen. They are easily recognised by the vertical stripes on the body and the spiny dorsal fin which has a black spot at the back. When young, perch swim together in large shoals but, as the fishes grow bigger, the shoals get smaller until the oldest fish are solitary. Young perch eat mainly insect larvae and crustaceans but turn to catching other fish when full grown.

As pond inhabitants fish have the additional interest that they can be caught on rod and line and very often eaten. Nearly every fish mentioned in this chapter is eaten, apart from the loaches, rudd and the very bony chub. On the Continent many of the edible fishes are netted commercially or farmed but, with the exception of trout and salmon, there is little demand for freshwater fish in Britain.

7

AMPHIBIANS AND REPTILES

Amphibians and reptiles are not everybody's favourite pets. Cold blooded, clammy skinned or scaly, sometimes venomous, they often evoke feelings of disgust or fear. Yet both classes of animal have their devotees who lavish as much care on them as any aquarist gives to his 'tropicals'. And surely tadpoles must be the most commonly kept of all wild animals. There can be few people outside city centres who have not fished for frog-spawn and taken it home to hatch, watching the tadpoles develop into baby frogs.

AMPHIBIANS

There are six native British amphibians, the common frog, the common toad, the rarer natterjack toad, and three newts. The frog and the toads are stout-bodied, with long hindlegs and are tailless. Toads are distinguishable from frogs by the warty, dry skin and by their spawn being laid in strings rather than in clumps. However, there are hundreds of anurans (literally 'tail-less ones') in the world and the names frog and toad have been handed out rather arbitrarily. The second group of amphibians, the caudates or 'tailed ones', includes the slender, long-tailed newts, as well as various salamanders, the mudpuppy, the olm and the sirens of other countries.

A common European frog lays a thousand or more eggs in one batch, a mass of spawn that dwarfs the parent frog. This would appear to be a case of a quart fitting into, or in this case, coming out of, a pint pot but the paradox is easily resolved : the jelly surrounding each egg is applied as a thin layer inside the frog's body and swells up only when it comes into contact with water. This swelling led to a strange country phenomenon, hardly ever seen nowadays because frogs are now comparatively rare. Farmers and shepherds who used to find lumps of whitish jelly mysteriously scattered over the ground assumed that it had fallen from the sky and called it Star-Slime or Rot of the Stars. When the matter was eventually investigated by a zoologist, he found that Star-Slime was no more than frogspawn jelly. Huge numbers of frogs had been eaten and their jelly-producing glands had passed through the predator's body undigested, then been voided onto the ground where they swelled with dew or rain.

The jelly of frogspawn forms an important protective layer around each egg. It buoys the spawn to the surface of the

24 Edible frogs have been introduced to several places in southern England

pond where it stays until hatching. It prevents the eggs from being eaten, cushions them from mechanical damage and keeps them warm. The black eggs absorb the sun's heat and the insulation of the jelly stops this heat from escaping. The increased warmth is important for speeding the development of the eggs and it is easy to demonstrate that spawn develops more rapidly in warm water by noting the time of appearance of particular organs or measuring growth of the body. The spawn will even warm the surrounding water. Place two jars of water in a well-lit but cool place and add frogspawn to one. The water containing frogspawn will be a degree or more warmer, but be careful not to place the spawn in direct sunlight or it will get cooked. Be sure also not to cram too much spawn into the jar because the spawn needs oxygen and will suffocate if deprived.

A hand lens reveals the stages of development in the eggs, well worth following because we can watch, in outline, the first steps of development of all vertebrates, including ourselves. In essence, human beings start life in the same way as a frog.

The newly fertilised frog egg is a plain sphere, dark above and pale underneath. After a short time, the sphere divides vertically into 2 hemispheres, then divides again at right angles to form 4 segments. The next split is horizontal, separating 4 smaller, dark sections on the upper side of the egg from 4 larger whitish sections underneath which become the yolk. More divisions lead to 16 and 32 sections, followed by a series of irregular divisions that turn the egg into an embryo consisting of a hollow sphere called a blastula. The next stage is for the blastula to turn into the gastrula by the dark cells forming a skin over the pale yolky cells except for one small circle which remains pale. Gradually a slit forms and deepens until the embryo has become a double-walled sphere with a hole in one end. This is an important stage because it marks the formation of all the basic body tissues and organs. Now the embryo gradually elongates and assumes the shape of the tadpole, until, after about two weeks, it is ready to hatch.

The newly hatched tadpole is barely able to wriggle and

clings to the jelly by means of a cement secreted from a 'sucker' on the head. The jelly continues to act as a protection for several days but eventually the tadpoles transfer themselves to a water plant or to the side of the aquarium. When first hatched, the mouth does not connect with the gut and the tadpole lives on its remaining yolk. When the mouth does become functional, the tadpole starts to feed on minute algae which it scrapes up with horny jaws. The mouth can be seen working as the tadpole browses over the aquarium glass. Unfortunately, tadpoles frequently come to grief because they are not fed. They need nurturing like any other pet and the first step is not to overstock the pond or aquarium.

Meanwhile the tadpole breathes through a set of feathery gills, while a second set of internal gills are already beginning to develop. A fold of skin, the operculum, grows over the external gills and closes completely except for a single opening, the spiracle. Now the tadpole respires like a fish, taking water in through its mouth, passing it over the new gills and out of the spiracle. By this time the sucker has disappeared and the long, coiled gut can be seen through the skin. The next stage is for the limbs to grow. The hindlegs appear first because the forelegs are developing under the operculum. One foreleg eventually sprouts through the operculum while the other bursts through the skin.

The tadpole is now changing into a land animal. Its tail is gradually absorbed, lungs replace the gills and the tadpole adopts a carnivorous way of life. It catches small water insects and crustaceans and, if food is short, turns cannibal, thereby regulating its own numbers. If food is not supplied to captive tadpoles, very few will reach the final stage of metamorphosis and emerge as froglets. When the time is nearly ripe for the froglets to come onto land, they gather in the shallows at the edge of the pond and await a good shower of rain, whereupon they swarm ashore. In the days when frogs were common, the appearance of thousands of froglets after rain led to reports of 'rains of frogs'. However, there are well authenticated records of true rains of frogs, when a tornado has whipped up the contents of a pond and deposited its contents on dry land. In 1921, the streets of north London were carpeted with froglets and other parts of the world have been similarly flooded with rains of toads, worms, crabs and winkles.

The development of a tadpole represents the change of an animal from an aquatic to a terrestrial way of life. The changes are both behavioural and physical and the adult amphibian usually returns to water only to breed. Many prefer damp surroundings but desert-living toads of America and Australia testify to the amphibians' conquest of dry land. A major hazard for amphibians is drying up but they can avoid the worst of a drought by burrowing into the soil where, even in deserts, the temperature is low and humidity is high only a few inches down. Desert frogs and toads of Australia can lose water equivalent to over 40 per cent of their body weight and some species store water in the bladder, absorbing it into the body as required.

While we are on the subject of survival in difficult circumstances, there is an oft-repeated story of live toads being found in cavities of rocks or tree trunks. A quarryman or woodman has cut open a seemingly solid rock or trunk and a toad has crept out. The inference is that the luckless creature has miraculously survived years of imprisonment but this was proved to be impossible some 150 years ago. Francis Buckland, a naturalist whose intense curiosity about animal life was assuaged by copious observation and experiment, took the trouble to immure some toads in blocks of stone and in an apple tree. They did not live long. The explanation for the apparently immortal toads immured in wood or stone is that, when very small, they crept into a nook or cranny and were then unable to get out. Whoever split the stone or sawed the wood did not examine it in advance for a hole and probably did not bother to check after the toad had come to light.

The word amphibian commemorates the double life of these animals that must return to water to breed and develop, betraying their fishy ancestry. The earliest days of spring see the amphibians making for their spawning grounds in ponds, quiet streams, the edges of lakes and even in drains and puddles. Some return annually to traditional places and new houses are sometimes invaded by frogs or toads looking for the pond or marsh which had been filled in to provide a building site. There may be regular migrations across country using landmarks or the position of stars for navigation and the route becomes marked by corpses where it crosses a road. Each year a scattering of run-over bodies shows the fidelity to migration route and destination.

The common European toad is one such regular migrant. The males are the first to move and they take up position in the water to await the larger females. The aim of each male is to seize a female under the arms and cling to her back until she spawns, so a scrum develops around each female as she arrives. Some females have already collected a male *en route* but they will attract yet more on arrival and females may even drown under the mass of struggling males. The mating position is called amplexus and male frogs and toads attempt to embrace any suitably sized object. If another male is clasped it will kick and croak to show the mistake. The female is recognised by her swollen, egg-filled body. Amplexus lasts for about a day, until egg-laying is completed. As the eggs are extruded, the male sheds his sperms, his position in amplexus bringing his cloaca close to that of the female to ensure that fertilisation takes place.

After she has shed her load of eggs, the female shrinks visibly and is then free to leave the water as the males appreciate her thinness. Males stay in the water for some time, so that it always looks as if there is a preponderance of males in the population. Some will mate more than once, so presumably others will fail to mate at all. This is usual when animals are not monogamous and there is probably some form of competition among the males that decides who will get the chance to mate.

25 Common toads mating. The male clasps the female so that he can fertilise the strings of eggs

The voice of frogs and toads signals rivalry towards other males and attracts females, so an amphibian's croaking is the equivalent of a bird's song. The sound is made with the vocal cords, by shuttling air to and fro between the lungs and inflatable pouches in cheeks or throat. The British frog and toad are feeble croakers but elsewhere in the world the amphibian chorus is maddening in its intensity and monotony. Each species has its individual call by which it can be recognised. The leopard frog of North America has three distinct calls: one directs other frogs to the pond, a second is uttered by the male as he approaches the female to induce her to let him clasp her and a third is a warning given by the male when clasped by another.

Frogs and toads do not feed during their spell in the spawning pond. When on land they hunt insects and other small invertebrates, using eyesight which is keen but limited. The nervous network in the retina of a frog's eye has special circuits that are triggered only by small, moving objects. This ties neatly with the observation that frogs only catch small, moving animals. Their diet contains a large proportion of active animals such as flies, beetles and spiders. Frogs just do not see motionless animals and a frog will starve when surrounded by dead flies.

As well as catching its prey, a frog must avoid being eaten itself, making split-second escapes to safety. When disturbed, it leaps without hesitation. But where to? An aimless leap earns only a temporary respite from danger. Here again the frog is equipped with a simple nervous mechanism that triggers and guides its behaviour. If a frog is shut in a box, black inside and with a window at one end, it will jump through the window and not bang its head on the sides or roof. (It may need a prod to make it move.) The frog is steering towards the light. With a pair of windows, the box can be used to test the frog's vision. Place coloured sheets of thin plastic in front of the windows, a different colour for each window, and illuminate them from behind. The frog will prefer to jump towards certain colours. Frogs prefer blue to green or yellow, jumping towards a dim blue light rather than to bright green or yellow light. The response is not 100 per cent accurate but the frogs jump towards blue rather than green eight or nine times out of ten.

What is the value of jumping towards blue? It seems likely that this colour will guide the frog, which normally lives around the edge of water among green grass and under green trees, to the safety of the pond. Even on an overcast day, water transmits more blue light than the surrounding vegetation, and so acts as a beacon.

The courtship and mating of newts is altogether a different affair from the clumsy embraces of frogs and toads. The male courts with a fluttering dainty dance and the female lays her eggs one at a time, both actions making newts charming animals

26 Larva of a smooth newt, with its gills almost absorbed, swimming among stems of Canadian pondweed

to keep and observe in an aquarium. At the onset of the breeding season the male newt grows an enlarged fin, his courtship dress in which he parades to attract the female's attention. The next step is to face his chosen one and thrash his tail or fold it double and quiver it rapidly. The beating of the tail throws a current of water at the female and carries secretions from the male's body to stimulate her. Fertilisation of the eggs is accomplished without an embrace. The male deposits a sperm packet on the ground and the female picks it up in her cloaca. Careful co-ordination is needed to synchronise the handover. The female moves behind the male so that her snout touches the tip of his tail. The sperm is extruded and the male moves forward precisely one body length so that, when the female follows him, her cloaca will be directly over the sperm pocket. Fertilisation is therefore internal and, when the eggs are ready to be laid, the female newt noses among the waterweeds in search of suitable leaves on which to lay them. She grasps a leaf with her hind-legs, lays an egg on it and folds the leaf over, sticking it down so that the egg can develop in safety.

REPTILES

The amphibians are animals that are striving to cut their links with their aquatic past, and completely successful land-living has been achieved by their descendants, the reptiles. Reptiles have a fully waterproof skin and their excretory system is more economical as regards the body's water supply. Amphibians excrete urea which needs to be flushed through the kidneys with a copious supply of water, whereas reptiles excrete uric acid that can be voided as a semi-solid mass. The main secret

27 Common toad after an encounter with a grass snake. It has inflated its body and straightened its legs so that the snake cannot swallow it

of the reptiles' success is that the egg has a leathery or chalk shell to prevent it drying up. As a result, reptiles are as common in deserts as amphibians are rare, but a number of reptiles have reverted to an aquatic existence. These include the crocodiles, the water tortoises or turtles and some snakes.

The only British reptile that qualifies as an aquatic species is the grass snake, sometimes called the water snake. It has two close relatives in North America that are called water snakes. Grass snakes are frequently found in damp hollows and marshes and are good swimmers. It is not an uncommon sight to see a grass snake slipping through the water, particularly during the main hunting period in the early morning. It swims with powerful side-to-side movements of the body with the head held well clear of the water. The spreading ripples make the snake look larger than it really is. It will dive after prey and can stay submerged for at least twenty minutes.

The prey of grass snakes is mainly frogs, where these are still abundant, followed by newts, fishes and tadpoles. Lizards, voles, mice, worms and young birds are also taken. Toads are usually avoided because of the poison in their skin (if a dog picks up a toad it will soon drop it and pour out streams of saliva to clear its mouth). The toad's second line of defence is to blow up the body and straighten its legs so that it appears to be standing on stilts. A grass snake swallows its prey whole and has difficulty in getting its mouth around the inflated toad. The grass snake, in turn, has its own means of defence. When handled it is liable to give off an unpleasant smelling secretion from its cloaca. It also blows up its body, hisses and strikes as if it were a venomous snake. This is complete bluff, as the grass snake is harmless. The third line of defence is also bluff. The snake shams dead, rolling onto its back with mouth open and tongue hanging out. The theory behind this behaviour is that many predators will not touch carrion; they eat only freshly killed animals and so leave the 'dead' snake alone. The snake is determined to look dead because, if turned right way up, it will immediately roll on its back again.

8

BIRDS AND MAMMALS

Open water is an attraction for many birds and mammals. Tracks at the water's edge show the need of badgers for drinking water. House martins visit muddy banks to get material for their nests. Swallows and swifts dip down to hawk for insects over the water and ponds with good growths of reed or bulrush attract their own birdlife community. Here reed buntings and sedge warblers nest and many small birds – swallows, sparrows and wagtails, for instance – gather to roost in large numbers. Such creatures must, however, fall outside the ranks of true pond-dwellers as they are not designed for the aquatic life and are only casual visitors compared with those birds and mammals that spend their lives in or around water.

DUCKS AND SWANS

Ducks are the most characteristic birds of fresh water and, indeed, ponds are often known as duckponds whether or not they actually house any ducks. The most familiar of ducks, one might say The Duck, is the mallard, once called 'wild duck' when the word mallard referred to the drake alone. The bright colours of the mallard drake, with glossy green head, white neck ring, purple, white-bordered speculum on the wings and curled tail feathers, add a touch of rainbow brilliance to a pond. At the height of summer, these gaudy males seem to disappear, as they assume the eclipse plumage from July to early September, and are distinguishable from the females only by darker, more even colouring of the crown and back.

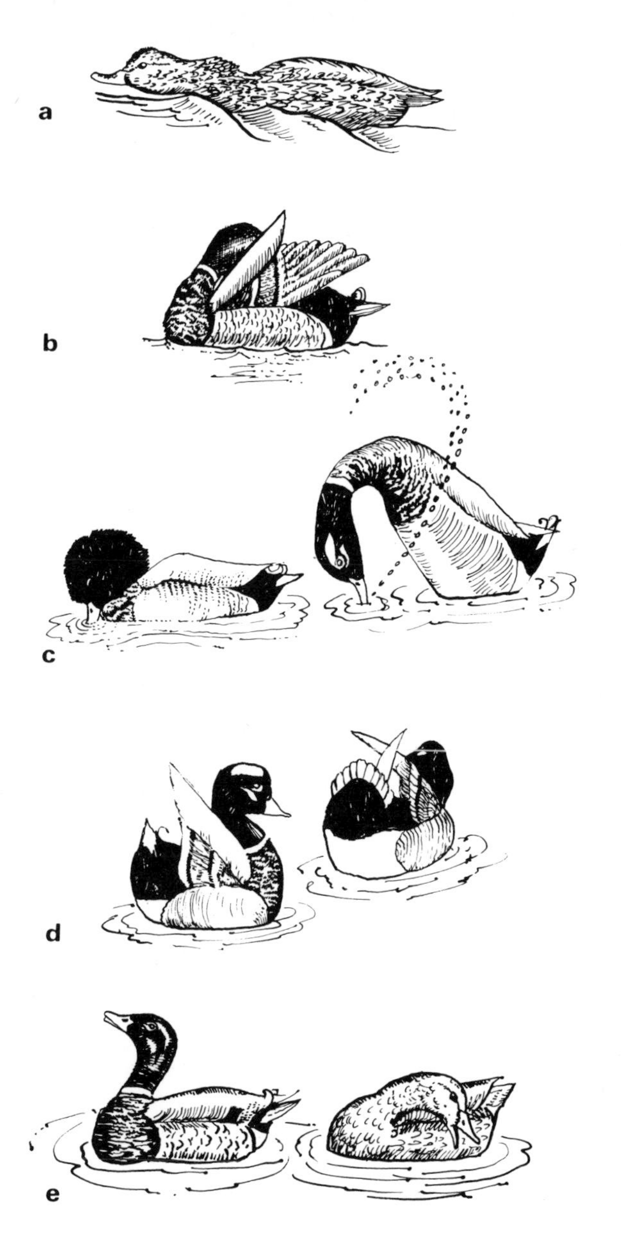

28 Mallard displays: (a) Duck 'nod-swimming'; (b) Drake 'mock-preening'; (c) Drakes 'grunt-whistling'; (d) Drakes 'head-up-tail-up'; (e) Duck inciting drake

When the drakes return to their full plumage, courtship displays begin. Pairing is accompanied by a ritual ceremonial and is initiated by the duck which paddles among the drakes with a display known as 'nod-swimming' or 'coquette swimming', with neck outstretched and head nodding. The reaction of nearby drakes is to bunch together and display to her with stereotyped actions that signal one mallard's emotions and intentions to the others. For instance, there is 'mock-preening' in which a drake lifts one wing and reaches behind with its bill as if to preen, but, instead rubs its bill against the wing to make a rattling noise. This action shows off the purple speculum to its best advantage. 'Mock-drinking' is a peace gesture when two drakes meet head on. Other displays include the 'grunt whistle', in which the drake thrusts his head into the water then throws the head back with a spray of droplets while, at the same time, uttering a low whistle followed by a grunt. The 'head-up-tail-up' display is self explanatory: the bird draws head and tail upwards and whistles. The display only lasts about one second and seems to be a very rapid mock-drinking.

Courtship reaches a new peak in late winter when the mallards can be seen associating in pairs. Mating is often promiscuous, and a duck may mate with a drake while her real mate looks on without interest. There are also cases of what appears to be rape, when several drakes chase one duck, forcing her underwater and apparently causing her great distress. The significance and function of these pursuits is not fully understood. Sometimes a drake drives away the female of a neighbouring pair while her mate follows but on other occasions the duck may be pursued by half-a-dozen drakes. There is a suggestion that this apparent rape is not so much an assault as a means by which the duck selects the most vigorous drake as father of her ducklings. However, as 'rapes' sometimes take place after the duck has laid her eggs, this cannot be the complete explanation.

Shortly after successful mating the duck retires to a thicket, usually fairly near water, where she makes her nest of grasses

29 Mute swan landing on a pond. Its extended feet act as brakes and send a shower of spray

and leaves mixed with feathers and fine down. Then she settles to lay ten to twelve eggs which she incubates by herself. The drake does, however, stay nearby and he may keep the family company when the duck leads her ducklings to water.

Mallards are dabbling ducks as are the teal, wigeon and shoveller. Dabblers feed on the surface of the water, sometimes upending to reach the bottom but rarely diving, and they also feed on land. The bill is provided with transverse rows of horny ridges along the outer margin and it is used to filter food from water or mud, much in the same way a blue whale uses its fringe of baleen plates to filter masses of krill, small shrimp-like animals, from the sea.

The mute swan, which certainly is not mute, was originally a wild bird. It became semi-domestic during the Middle Ages when all swans were the property of the Crown or certain privileged people and organisations. Ownership of a swan was established by a series of notches on the bill and cygnets are still marked on the river Thames in the traditional ritual of 'swan-upping'. The male mute swan, or cob, defends a territory on a stretch of river or a pond from which he drives all opposition. He can be seen parading magnificently through the water with simultaneous strokes of his legs. Mute swans mate for life and the cob stays near the nest of piled vegetation while his mate, the pen, incubates the eggs. The cob incubates only when the pen needs to feed and, as the eggs hatch, he leads the cygnets to water while the pen sits on the remainder of the clutch. The family stays together for some time before the cygnets are chased away.

COOTS, MOORHENS AND OTHERS

Coots prefer the larger ponds and lakes where they can be seen swimming in groups. They are generally more aquatic than moorhens, as is shown by the fleshy lobes on their toes which act as paddles. Moorhens have no webbing on their feet and spend more time on land, where they can be seen feeding in meadows. The name moorhen is a corruption of 'merehen', from the Old English word for lake. Coots and moorhens feed mainly on water plants, which are supplemented by small animals, including fish. Coots dive beneath the water, to bring masses of plants to the surface where they can be picked through and eaten at leisure.

The breeding of coots and moorhens is similar in many respects and has some interesting features. Both birds are aggressive in defence of their territories. When rivals meet, they sit back on their tails and thrash with their feet, sending up a spray of water. Flocks of coot have also been seen using this tactic to scare away predatory birds. Once arguments have been settled, the birds settle down to a truly admirable way of life. Each pair builds a platform of vegetation, among reeds or in waterside vegetation, with a cup-shaped depression in the centre. The eggs are incubated by both male and female and vigilance is needed by the parent birds because a rise in water level could be disastrous. When there is a flood, the birds add more vegetation to lift the eggs or chicks above the rising waters. When the flood subsides, the nest is left high and dry on a compact column. Baby moorhens have been seen taking material gathered by their parents and working it into the nest. Apart from being a neat piece of family co-operation, this behaviour shows how nest-building is instinctive. Most birds do not attempt to build a nest until sexually mature but these moorhen chicks are competent at working material into the nest shortly after hatching. Co-operation continues after they have left the nest and can fly. Young moorhens and coots rear two or three broods of young each year and the young of earlier broods stay with their parents and help feed their younger brothers and sisters.

Two fish-hunting birds associated with ponds are the heron and kingfisher. Herons breed in colonies, nesting at the top of tall trees or on cliff faces. Kingfishers too, will sometimes nest at a distance from water but their burrows are more usually in the steep bank of a pond or stream. Whereas herons are stealthy stalkers, kingfishers are divers, plunging headlong with a glitter of blue plumage to seize a fish or water insect. From the bottom of its dive, the kingfisher regains the surface by 'flying' through the water and erupting into the air without pausing. Larger fish are carried to a perch and beaten to subdue them.

The little grebe or dabchick is the commonest but most retiring of the grebes and may be found on small ponds. Grebes

30 Great crested grebe showing breeding season plumage (left) and normal plumage

are principally hunters of fish and small aquatic animals but they also take some plant food. They build well-hidden nests of vegetation and carry their young on their backs as a protection against pike. Both sexes of the great crested grebe sport plumes and 'ear tufts' during the breeding season and these are shown off during courtship dances that take place on the water. At the simplest there is 'head shaking' but the 'penguin dance' and the 'cat display' are elaborate performances. In the penguin dance, both birds dive and come to the surface with weed in their bills. Then they rear up breast to breast and sway from side to side. The cat display consists of the grebe lowering its head, wings spread out with their leading edges turned down.

VOLES AND SHREWS

Pond mammals contrast strongly with the birds. They lack the showy plumage and elaborate displays and they lead secretive lives. Few mammals live in or beside inland waters and they show themselves less than do water birds. Perhaps because they are hard to find, the sighting of a water mammal or the discovery of its tracks is particularly exciting. Both require patient observation that results in a gradual piecing together of the animal's life.

The water vole is easier to watch than other water mammals. Its presence is given away by burrows and cropped 'lawns' where it has been feeding on the bank. A loud 'plop' tells that the

31 The water vole lives in a hole in the bank and comes out to feed on waterside plants

vole has dropped into water and a quiet wait is often rewarded with the sight of it ploughing away across stream or pond. The water vole is almost the same size as a rat and it is often called the water rat. It is a vole because it has a blunt snout and the small ears and eyes are almost hidden in the fur. However, the water vole is probably the original rat as rat is a Saxon word and true rats did not arrive in Britain until the Middle Ages. Brown rats confuse the situation because they often live along river banks, where their tracks and droppings may be mistaken for those of water voles.

Although quite an accomplished swimmer, the water vole seems to be aquatic only in Britain, and lives on dry land in Europe. Even in waterside habitats the water vole shows its terrestrial habits by the extent of its burrow system which may cause extensive damage to the banks of dykes and drains. The hole in the bank leads into a long winding passage with food storage and sleeping chambers. Digging is accomplished with the forefeet, while the teeth are used to remove stones. In the thick vegetation are runs, like those made by rabbits through herbage, which act as bolt-ways.

The water vole has regular meal times. Its presence is given away by occasional ripples spreading out from the edge of the weeds or by the jerky movements of one stem, when there is no breeze to stir them. The stem shakes more and more, then slowly slides out of sight as the vole draws it down to feed on its leaves. As meals are regular it is easy to time visits to pond or stream to coincide with water-vole activity. While feeding, the voles seem oblivious of their surroundings, but this is an illusion. Water voles have poor eyesight but their hearing is excellent; snap a twig and the vole disappears in a twinkling.

Rarely seen far from a pond, stream or marsh, the water shrew is more at home in water than the water vole. Its body also shows more adaptations for an aquatic life. Neither vole nor shrew has webbed feet but the water shrew's toes are bordered with bristles which make them more efficient paddles. The tail is also fringed with a keel of hairs and is flattened from

32 A rare visitor to ponds, an otter eats a fish. Note the whiskers, the small ears and the eyes set high on the head

side to side to make a good rudder. Water shrews are rarely seen in open water but when they do swim out their bodies appear silvery from the air trapped in the fur. Their presence is given away more often by a high-pitched squeaking from the depths of bankside vegetation. Like the squeak of bats, shrews' calls are near the upper limit of human hearing and they often cannot be heard by older people whose sense of hearing is beginning to fade.

Water shrews are restlessly active, having bouts of furious activity alternating with rest. Small water animals are seized and taken to the bank where they can be chewed up. Large animals are subdued by a poisonous bite. A mammal usually dries its fur as soon as it comes ashore so as to restore the insulation and keep warm. The water shrew has so little time to spare from foraging that it dries its fur while eating, whereas most animals perform their toilet at leisure after their meal.

9

PLANT LIFE

A pond's aesthetic appeal depends largely on the plants that grow in and around it. They turn the pond from a water-filled hole in the ground to a thing of beauty, the fresh green of the leaves and the delicate colours of the flowers contributing to an atmosphere of quiet and coolness on a hot summer's day. Prosaically, and of more importance, plants help to oxygenate the water so that aquatic animals can breathe. They provide food and shelter and their decaying remains fertilise later generations of plants. The abundance of vegetation depends on the fertility of the water and surrounding soil. In eutrophic (nutrient-rich) conditions with plenty of nutrients and where the water is shallow a rich variety of plants can flourish, but in the oligotrophic (mineral deficient) waters of a steep-sided mountain tarn, the flora is poor. Shade is also important. Overhanging branches cut down the light available for photosynthesis in the pond and falling leaves accumulate as a thick slimy layer whose decomposition effectively removes all oxygen from the water. Woodland ponds where trees overhang the water are consequently disappointing as very little in the way of animals and plants lives there.

Apart from knowing that water weeds are a good place to search for animal life, plants are inclined to be overlooked by pond hunters. This is a pity because plants have plenty to offer the naturalist. In the same way as we can see how the habits and form of an animal suit it for a particular way of life, so it is possible to relate a plant's form, flowering and propagation to its environment. And water plants are particularly instructive in this respect. They are descended from land-dwelling plants so we can see what changes they have had to undergo to take up an aquatic existence.

As basis of comparison between land and water plants let us look at a 'basic flowering plant'. It is made up of three parts: stem, roots and leaves. The stem is a combination of skeleton and blood system. It has a core of tissue called xylem which consists of water-transporting tubes interspersed with tough fibres to give mechanical strength and rigidity. Surrounding the xylem is another tissue, the phloem, which carries food materials. The leaves are factories for the manufacture of sugars by the process of photosynthesis. Their green colour is the pigment chlorophyll which absorbs the sun's energy to drive the chemical reactions of photosynthesis, and the flattened shape gives a large surface for absorbing sunlight. The roots anchor the plant in the soil and the minute hairs that cover the surface of every rootlet absorb water and salts from the soil.

Water is the basis of the plant's economy. It is an essential constituent of all living tissues, which contain about 80 per cent water, but plants also need water as a raw material in photosynthesis and a flow of water is needed to carry nutrient salts from root to leaf. Water pressure also helps the fibres to keep the leaves and stem rigid. If denied water, the plant wilts and dries up, but water loss is prevented by a waxy cuticle that forms a waterproof skin. Water circulates through the plant by evaporation at the leaf surface drawing a stream of water through the plant from the roots. Called transpiration, this water movement must be maintained if photosynthesis and the transport of salts is to continue to take place. It is regulated by stomata which are minute, adjustable pores in the surface of the leaf. If the roots cannot get enough water from the soil, the stomata close up to reduce water loss and prevent wilting. The stomata's second function is to allow atmospheric oxygen and carbon dioxide to percolate into the plant tissues for respiration and photosynthesis.

Plants reproduce by flowering. One flower may contain both

male stamens and female stigma or the sexes may be separate in male and female flowers. In any case, pollen from the stamens has to reach the stigma for fertilisation and for seed to set. Flowers with both stamens and stigma can fertilise themselves but it is usual for cross-fertilisation to take place by the pollen being transferred to another flower by wind or insects. When the seeds have been formed they must then be transported to a suitable place for germination. A variety of agencies may be involved. Wind carries sycamore keys, birds carry blackberry fruits, and sticky burdock seeds are carried in animal fur. Some plants augment flowering or sexual reproduction by asexual propagation – the equivalent of *Hydra* budding (p 32). So we have the daffodil's bulbs, the iris's rhizomes and the runners of strawberries in which new plants spring directly from the old plant.

Aquatic flowering plants have modified this basic plan of form and they function in several ways. Most kinds still need contact with atmospheric air to breathe and for the dissemination of pollen, but life under water has led to some important changes. In some ways, life in water is easier for plants than life on dry land but it has its drawbacks. There is, for instance, water in abundance so there is no danger of wilting (unless the pond dries up), but oxygen can run short in ponds and plants living beneath the surface with no access to atmospheric air run the danger of suffocation.

Because water plants are surrounded by the liquid, waterproofing and water-conserving characteristics lose their importance. Submerged parts of the plant do not need the waterproofing cuticle and, because water can then be absorbed over the whole surface area, roots are not so essential. So we find that many water plants have weak root systems and can survive uprooting. Cuticle and stomata are confined to parts of the plant which break the surface. A waterlily has no cuticle on the underside of its floating leaves but there is a thick layer on the exposed face. The cuticle not only prevents water loss, it is unwettable, like the wax polish of a car, so water always runs off the leaf leaving the surface dry and air free to enter the stomata.

Aquatic plants do not need a flow of water from root to leaf so they can reduce the amount of water-transporting xylem tissue in the stem. In land plants mechanical strength is as important as water transport and the stem and leaves must be held rigid, but an aquatic plant is supported by the surrounding water so there is no need for rigidity. On the contrary, flexibility is a virtue for plants exposed to moving water, either as the steady flow of a stream or as turbulence set up by the wind. Reduction of the xylem is, therefore, a characteristic of water plants, but there are usually a few strands running through the stem to give tensile strength and so prevent the plant being torn apart. The effect of the current is reduced by streamlining the leaves, so we find long, slender plants in streams and rivers lying along the direction of the current.

The absence of cuticle on the submerged parts of an aquatic plant means that dissolved gases and salts can be absorbed by the tissues of leaf and stem. Carbon dioxide is plentiful in solution so the plant can easily get all it needs through the leaf surface. Text-books have always said that the reason why many water plants have leaves divided into fine fronds is to increase the surface area for gas absorption, but it now seems that this is not the whole story and that the leaf-form of water plants depends more on the amount of mineral salts in the water and of carbohydrates produced by photosynthesis. Some water plants also use bicarbonate in the water, as well as dissolved carbon dioxide gas, for photosynthesis and excess bicarbonate sometimes gathers as a white encrustation of calcium carbonate (lime) on the leaves. Called marl, it is found on stoneworts, water soldier, pondweeds and others.

We have seen that there are times when pond water is very low in oxygen, so the supply of oxygen for respiration can be a problem. If the plant stands clear of the water surface, air can enter the stomata and diffuse down the stem to the submerged parts. All plant tissues contain tiny spaces which allow gases to diffuse through the interior, but water plants also have a special air transport tissue composed of star-shaped cells which fit together loosely so that there are large spaces between them. Sometimes these cells develop in to a large air-filled tube running the length of the plant. Cut a waterlily stem and the tubes can be seen taking up almost half the stem. The airspaces also help the plant to float and are an oxygen reserve for respiration at night when photosynthesis has shut down. They are particularly important for plants that stand rooted in mud. Roots need oxygen as much as the rest of the plant and the roots of land plants get oxygen from air that percolates between the soil particles. They may die if the ground becomes waterlogged so a special air supply is vital for pond plants which may have their roots in mud totally devoid of oxygen.

Because submerged plants can absorb nutrient salts through their leaves, the root's most important function is to anchor the plant. The absorption of salts by roots is, however, necessary for life in mineral deficient water. An exception is the rootless bladderwort which floats in infertile bog pools. It makes good the deficiency by turning carnivore. Bladderwort is distinguished by air-filled bladders on special branches. The bladders act like living mousetraps for catching small animals. When a water flea blunders against the trigger, a trapdoor flies open and the luckless crustacean is swept in on a rush of water, whereupon it is smothered in enzymes which digest its internal organs, leaving only the empty husk to be ejected.

POLLINATION AND DISPERSAL

For the majority of plants living in ponds and streams the pattern of pollination is no different from that found in land plants. The flowers bloom on special stems which emerge from the water to hold them aloft. The water milfoils and pondweeds are wind pollinated and the waterlilies are visited by insects, such as caddis flies and beetles. However, other plants use water as a medium for carrying pollen to the stigma. The flowers of the Canadian pondweed open just at the surface and pollen grains are scattered onto the water by the explosive rupturing of the stamens. The grains have a fine hairy covering that makes them unwettable like the hairy bodies of water insects (p 47) and they are wafted by the wind across the surface to the female flowers.

A very few plants have underwater flowers. They are the botanical equivalent of the whales in severing all links with dry land. One such plant is the hornwort whose flowers nestle inconspicuously in the angle between the stem and the fan of bristly leaves. The male flower has ten to twenty stamens which break off when ripe and float to the surface. There they split open and release their pollen which sinks slowly to the bottom. Only by chance will some come to rest on the single stigma of a female flower. Wind and water pollination mechanisms have much in common, particularly in the chancy nature of releasing vast masses of pollen into the vagaries of the aerial or aquatic medium. Only a minute percentage of pollen grains fall on the stigmas, in contrast to insect pollination where pollen is carried directly to the stigma. Some water plants apparently use both wind and water pollination. Whorled milfoil usually flowers underwater but sometimes it sends its flowers above the surface if the water is shallow. On the other hand fennel-leaved pondweed has aerial flowers as a rule but it may occasionally flower and fruit underwater.

Living in water offers good opportunities for the dispersal of seeds. This is a problem for land plants unless the fruits are light enough to be blown by the wind. A water plant can drop its fruits into the water and they are carried away by the current or swept over the surface by wind. The floating fruits of the yellow waterlily gave rise to the plant's old country name of 'brandy bottle'; they are flask-shaped and even smell alcoholic when ripe. The fruits break away from the parent plant and float about before falling apart to release the seeds. The fruit of the white waterlily, by contrast, sinks before disintegrating and the seeds surface and disperse before resinking and germinating.

33 Flower of yellow waterlily on the left with water crowfoot, a member of the buttercup family, on the right. Between are a few fronds of duckweed

The spread of water plants is assisted when their seeds are carried by animals to new stretches of water. Some seeds, like those of the bur-reed are bristly or sticky and get tangled in fur or feathers. Others survive the passage through the digestive system of ducks and germinate when passed, perhaps many miles from their starting point.

Despite these cunning devices for pollination and seed dispersal, many aquatic plants shun sexual reproduction and even when they flower may fail to set seed; but they make up for this by asexual propagation. This process is quite common among land plants but their runners, suckers or bulbs have to become rooted before they can be detached from the parent plant. Aquatic plants do not have this problem because the new plant can immediately draw its vital supplies from the water. The efficiency of vegetative propagation is amply demonstrated by the way a pond is covered with duckweed without the production of a single flower, and by the spread of Canadian pondweed through Britain. Only female plants were brought over from North America and, although a few male plants have been found since, sexual reproduction has never taken place. When Canadian pondweed first appeared, rivers, canals and drains became so choked that water transport and drainage were seriously hampered. The government's clearance programme did not get far, however, because each cut fragment of Canadian pondweed grows into a new plant. Luckily, but for some unknown reason, the plant suddenly became less vigorous and retreated of its own accord.

Before the onset of winter, floating vegetation disappears from the pond. The surface is a dangerous place in winter because frost can destroy plant tissues. The bottom, however, is more equable and the plants retreat there, either by dying back if they have good roots or underground stems, like the waterlilies, or by a special form of vegetative reproduction in which resting buds for shoots are formed. The resting buds of frogbit are different from those that produce the summer leaves, each containing an embryo plant and a reserve of starch. After spending the winter on the bottom, the embryo starts to develop and uses up its starch, so the bud becomes lighter and bobs back to the surface.

The duckweeds, as befits their simple anatomy, do not go to such lengths. Starch accumulates through the summer's photosynthesis until the fronds are too heavy to float. They spend the winter at the bottom and when the starch has been used up in respiration they float again.

The water soldier has a different flotation system. During the summer it collects an encrusting layer of marl on its leaves which eventually weighs it down so that it sinks. Next spring new leaves sprout. They have no lime and are buoyant so the plant bobs back to the surface. Bladderwort stops throwing out new leaves in autumn, and instead develops a tight bud of clustered leaves at the tip of each branch. The rest of the plant rots and falls apart, while the dense buds sink to the bottom. Then the buds start to grow, the leaves expand, air spaces develop and the buds rise to the surface.

PLANT COMMUNITIES

A pond's vegetation can be divided into communities or associations of species. Broadly, these coincide with the surface, midwater and bottom animal communities described in Chapter 2, together with the swamp and marsh communities of the pond's edge. Rather different plant communities are found in flowing water.

The pond may be so completely covered with floating plants that hardly any water surface can be seen. The commonest of these plants are the duckweeds which favour rich, very still waters. Sheets of duckweed can be a nuisance to the pond collector because every dip of the net brings up a coating of weed, but the plants deserve a close look before being scraped away. Apart from sheltering many small animals, the duckweeds represent a high point in the adaptation of flowering plants for an aquatic way of life. The common duckweed or duck's meat, so called because of its popularity with wildfowl, consists of a flat oval frond about 1/10in across. This is leaf-like rather than being a true leaf as it combines functions of both leaf and stem. From the frond hangs a single rootlet. Small flowers are sometimes to be found growing on the fronds particularly in shallow water during very hot sunny weather, where they give the duckweed a yellowish hue, but reproduction is usually by budding. This habit can be a nuisance in aquaria and garden ponds because one frond imported with other plants can lead to 100 per cent coverage of the water surface within a short space of time.

Two other kinds of free-floating flowering plants are the frogbit and the related water soldier. The frogbit has a rosette of kidney-shaped leaves and white flowers and is quite common in ponds and canals. The water soldier looks rather like a pineapple top

34 Water soldier

with stiff saw-edged leaves. For much of the time it lives just below the surface, balancing by its long hanger roots, but it surfaces to flower. In Britain water soldier is restricted to the ponds and ditches of eastern England but it is common on the continent where it may form a sward on still water. So dense is the growth on the waterways of Holland that, during World War II, British airmen mistook them for flat fields, perfect places for a forced landing until the splash showed otherwise.

The duckweeds and other free-floating plants are limited to the sheltered stretches where the wind cannot tear up the fronds and throw them ashore. Where there is no shelter, these species are replaced by plants which have floating or projecting leaves but also have long stems that reach to the bottom and are firmly anchored in the mud. Those with upstanding leaves and stems projecting above the water are called emergent plants.

Waterlilies are a familiar example of rooted, floating plants. Their leaves and stems die off in the autumn and are replaced in spring by a new growth sprouting from rhizomes buried in the mud. Water starwort is a cosmopolitan species which can either float freely or be rooted in the mud of shallow ponds and ditches. Water plantain is an emergent plant with a 3ft flower stem. Arrowhead is named after the three-spiked leaves that project from the water, but it also has two other kinds of leaf that lie beneath the surface – first a grass-like leaf which appears in spring to be followed by an oval, floating leaf, then finally the 'arrowhead'. Water dropwort, a member of the carrot family, Umbelliferae, has a similar division of aerial and submerged leaves.

35 Arrowhead

Even these rooted plants are affected by the wind to some extent. Whenever there is a steady blow, the water is set in motion with the result that the downwind end accumulates a scum of pollen grains, feathers, leaves and other flotsam. Quite small and apparently sheltered ponds can be stirred up if not protected by trees, and the water movement is sufficient to restrict the growth of floating and emergent plants to the quieter upwind margin.

The true bottom-dwelling plants are those rooted in mud with stems and leaves that remain submerged, except to thrust a flower head above water. They include the many pondweeds, milfoils, water violet and the stoneworts, all with divided hair-like leaves. The quillwort is a fern consisting of a bunch of sword-like fronds and looking quite unlike the common ferns of wood and hillside. It grows in the shallow mud covering the stony shores of nutrient-poor lakes and tarns.

Suspended in limbo, as it were, between rooted plants and the free-floaters on the surface, are the submerged, floating plants of midwater. We have already met the bladderwort. The hornwort is another rootless plant with whorls of threadlike leaves. It starts life loosely anchored to the bottom and later floats to the surface. The midwater is also the home of algae, including the single-celled diatoms and other organisms in the province of the microscopist, and the larger, filamentous green algae such as *Ulothrix* that grows in green masses in stagnant or running waters.

Around the edges of the pond there is a transition from aquatic to land habitats. If the banks are steep there is a sudden change, but a gently shelving edge to the pond encourages a rich mass of plants. First comes the swamp, an area covered with water except during the driest times and dominated by tall reeds, reedmace and bulrush, a fine retreat for ducks, coots and moorhens. Bogbean and flowering rush add to the colour of the swamps. Farther inland there is the marsh of waterlogged but nutrient-rich soil dominated by rushes, sedges, meadow-sweet and the yellow iris or flag. Marsh marigolds, or kingcups, water forget-me-nots and great willow-herb also live here as does water mint whose leaves smell like the garden variety.

Without man's active intervention, a pond naturally shrinks and disappears as swamp and marsh take over. If it is not kept clear by excavation and if there are no cattle to trample down the edges, the pond gradually fills with mud and accumulated vegetation. The sides gradually encroach on the centre until the only sign of the pond is a patch of marshy ground. The home of the moorhen, stickleback and waterboatman and breeding ground of frog and newt has disappeared. This natural process of infilling is called an aquatic succession, or hydrosere, and the stages can be seen in old ponds, disused canals, gravel pits and along the edges of lakes and slow-flowing rivers, where there is zonation of plants from floating plants in deep water through rooted plants in shallower water and swamp to marsh ending, if conditions are right, in dry land.

The plant succession starts from the moment that a pond is a raw hole in the ground, excavated for some reason or formed unintentionally like the outbreak of new ponds that pockmarked Europe through the indiscriminate scattering of high explosive in World War II. Microscopic algae are the first to appear, followed by the water plants that need little to anchor them: Canadian pondweed and starwort. Gradually the pond becomes a thriving biologic entity with dragonflies and other water insects making their homes there. As the plants die and rot down, mud accumulates and the pond becomes shallower. The true water plants disappear and reed, rushes and flags spring up. Their root systems help to bind the gathering mud until standing water disappears completely. Accumulation of organic debris from dead plants continues until ground level rises well above the water table and all signs of the pond have disappeared. A land-based plant community takes over and the spot becomes wooded, first with birch, willow and alder, then oak or other trees.

10

MAKING AND EXPLORING A POND

The loss of ponds throughout the countryside over the last couple of decades is now being checked by the renovation of old ponds and the construction of new ones, all in the interests of amenity. Likewise the disappearance of the old ponds that had formed an important home and refuge for many kinds of wildlife is being balanced by the ornamental ponds of suburbia. A pond is well worth having, even in a city backgarden.

If there are no ponds or streams nearby, the tyro collector need not be dismayed; he can make his own. It can be an old sink, bath or a hole in the ground lined with a sheet of polythene. Here, in the privacy of your own garden or in public, the field is open for simple, unarduous biological study.

POND MAKING

Dig a hole about 6ft across, circular, rectangular or oval according to preference. It is a good idea to have two depths, depending on the requirements of what you hope will live there. If visiting birds are to be an attraction, a shallow bathing area is needed, although you can compromise by making a small island which allows small birds to drink or paddle on its shores without danger of drowning. A deeper area gives space for pond plants and shelter for fish. A good compromise is to make the pond about 1ft deep with a 'deep end' of about 20in. Disposal of the earth may be a problem but there is usually some part of the garden that could do with some topsoil to level it. Or a rock garden can be built by the pond.

At one time all garden ponds were lined with concrete which is still the most permanent method. There are drawbacks, however. Concrete has to be well flushed after setting in to remove substances that are toxic to fish. It is also liable to cracking and may simply leak, although these last failings can now be cured with bituminous paints and cement-sealers. Nowadays concrete is generally dispensed with and waterproofing is effected by lining the hole with heavy duty polythene sheet. Care must be taken to avoid punctures and the edges of the sheet need disguising if the pond is to look attractive. An overhanging ring of paving slabs successfully masks the edges and looks very good for a formal garden pond but is a disadvantage for the naturalist's pond because the steep sides and overhang can act as a trap. Animals fall in and the pond becomes a mortuary for mice and hedgehogs that have come along for a drink. Neither can newly developed froglets get out to start their adult life. A death trap should be averted by angling the sides and hiding the polythene with a ring of sloping stones like a river embankment. As a compromise, a slipway can be constructed in part of the overhanging ring. An overflow pipe running between polythene and slabs is particularly useful in areas with a high rainfall.

Fitting out turns the pond from a mere basin of water to a fully fledged aquatic environment. Quite how it should be furnished depends on what is required. Some pond owners are bird enthusiasts and see a pond full of fishes as a tempting lure for herons and kingfishers. Fish fanciers take the opposite view and take steps to discourage feathered predators. It is said that an ornamental heron or stork of plastic or stone is a good deterrent for herons – they are shy of close company – but these are too much like a plastic gnome for some people's taste. Strands of thin green twine, nylon is the toughest and most inconspicuous, run around the pond about 6in above the ground will keep herons from the pond, if the loss of a few fish outweighs the pleasure of seeing a heron in the garden.

Water plants can be planted direct into soil laid on the bed

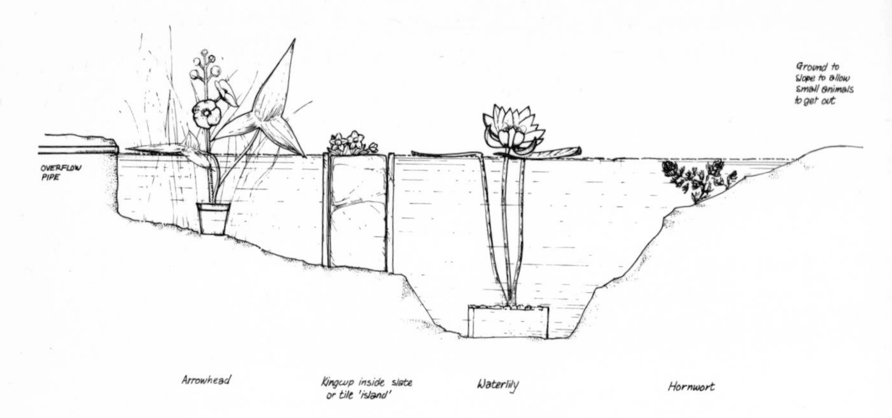

36 Section through a garden pond

of the pond but a neater method is to put the plants into pots or shallow trays of soil which are then placed as required. An advantage of this method is that the plants can be lifted for thinning or during pond clearance. Some of the more showy water plants will grow around the fringes of ponds, in the water-logged conditions of marshes and swamps, conditions which can be reproduced by filling one corner of the pond with soil behind a retaining wall of rocks or bricks. Yellow iris, amphibious bistort, kingcup and meadowsweet do well here. Good plants for deeper water include waterlilies, free floating hornwort, water-soldier and frogbit, and water starwort or Canadian pondweed whose value lies in its ability to oxygenate the water all the year round. Remember that it is now illegal to dig up wild plants without permission from the landowner.

If the sole aim of the pond is to keep fish, there is little point in introducing any other animal, except as fish food. And, of course, fish food is needed; goldfish food is convenient. Many kinds of fish will flourish in a pond – even trout which need plenty of oxygen and usually live in streams or large lakes – but overstocking must be avoided. Stocking can be improved by aerating the water with a fountain of the kind that circulates the water by an electric pump. Sticklebacks are as good a fish as any to have in a pond particularly if they can be persuaded to breed (Chapter 6). However, amphibians may be found to be more rewarding to keep than fish. For one thing they do not eat up all the other inhabitants. Then small quantities of frog-spawn can be introduced for the fun of watching tadpoles develop (Chapter 7) and a few newts swimming gracefully through the weeds are a great attraction. Pond snails are a must; they are very hardy and help clear up rubbish. Other invertebrates are a matter of choice or a matter of chance, depending on what can be captured locally and what drops in by itself.

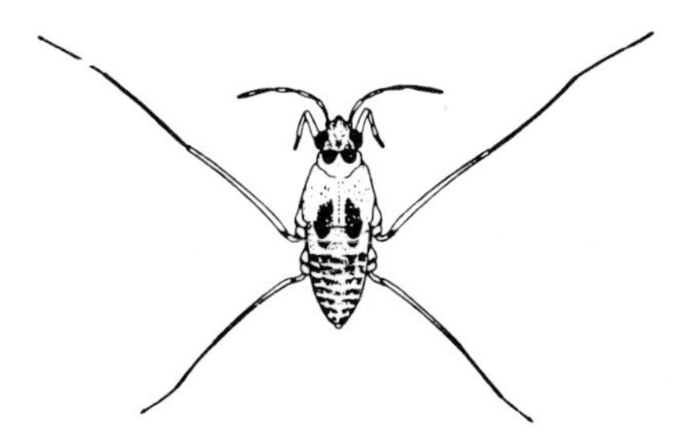

37 Pond skater – a water bug which may well appear in your pond

Even with the deliberate introduction of plants and animals, a pond will take some time to settle down. In fact, it is best not to leave it to its own devices, any more than a flowerbed is left untended. The pond must be nurtured and weeded for the best results, otherwise some species disappear while others run riot. A great nuisance, particularly in a new pond, is blooms of algae. Initially, the pond will be rich in nutrients from the soil surrounding the plants. Algae thrive on the nutrients and may choke the pond. This is more of a nuisance than a danger. Fish can live happily in a pond like pea soup but their presence is pointless if they cannot be seen. The algal bloom will eventually clear itself as nutrients are used up but its departure can be speeded by the careful application of copper sulphate or by using floating-leaved plants like waterlily or duckweed to inhibit algal growth by cutting off the light.

EXPLORING THE POND

With a village or farm pond nearby or a garden pond even more conveniently close at hand, the question arises as to what to do with it. Prodding around with a net to find what turns up gets boring and is definitely unprofitable. It is best to try and follow through systematic projects, with the proper collecting and recording of animals. For instance, how do the life-cycles of the insects fit in with the annual cycle of the pond? This and other questions can be answered by regular collection that shows how the fortunes of the inhabitants wax and wane, appearing in spring and disappearing in autumn and during droughts. It does not matter that this is a routine that has been carried out a hundred times elsewhere. Every pond is different from the last and is probably different itself from year to year. Moreover, the results of such collecting will bring to light problems and questions that stimulate further, more interesting, exploration, so that soon the whole family may become involved with 'their' pond.

Ideally, the study of a pond should start with a survey of its physical characters such as area and depth. This is obviously not so necessary for the regular, plastic-lined garden pond, but the information could be useful in a more natural pond. A survey does not take long and, once done, need not be repeated unless there is evidence of a change such as the gradual encroachment of swamp plants. All you need is an hour or so, spent with tape measure to map the shape of the pond, then sketch in the principal zones of swamp, reed, floating and emergent vegetation. Description of overhanging trees, inflow and outflow of water may be added. Inflow is particularly important if the water comes from a drain or off a road and so may carry pollutants. The nature of the underlying soil may also affect the pond's inhabitants. A profile of the pond can be constructed by wading or boating across with a measuring stick. If depth varies through the year, a fixed pole can be used as a 'tide gauge'. It is also useful to record the weather, both at the time and in the recent past. Is it cloudy and is there sufficient wind to create ripples on the surface? Has there been heavy rain in the past few days? It could dilute the pond's chemicals with fatal consequences to some animals. These factors influence the pond's animal life, as will the temperature of the water. It is interesting to compare the water temperature with the air temperature.

The interesting task of finding what lives in the pond should be approached with caution. When a heavy-footed collector lumbers up to the bank and prods around, warning ripples speed through the water. Pond skaters, fishes and moorhens scurry to safety and all the interesting animals will take refuge in the mud or the deepest recesses of the weeds so hardly anything is caught. For the best results approach cautiously, then sit and watch. On a sunny day this is the best part of the whole exercise. A sharp eye catches dragonflies emerging from their nymphal skins on the stems of emergent plants, or adults may be courting in tandem and settling to probe with the abdomen underwater in search of egg-laying sites. Moorhens creep out from the cover of bulrushes and fish swim just below the surface. If there is not too much waterweed, you can look down into the water and see waterboatmen, sticklebacks and leeches swimming through the water. Or a water-beetle larva paddles out from the weeds and sinks its pincer jaws into a tadpole.

During this initial period of idleness the pond's structure becomes apparent. The zones of the surface film, open water, perhaps the bottom mud if the water is very clear, and the various plant communities become alive and reveal some of their inhabitants. It is now time to investigate more closely, taking each zone in turn. Again, proceed gently. Thrashing around with the net scares the animals and stirs up mud. Investigate the surface film first by sweeping the net across the surface to pick up mosquito larvae, backswimmers and perhaps

Stenus beetles. These are members of the rove-beetle family that secrete a substance from the rear of the abdomen and slide across the water like the toy boats propelled by a lump of camphor in the stern. The open water is sampled by long, slow figure-of-eight sweeps. If a regular survey is being conducted, the change in abundance of animals can be gauged by making a set number of sweeps, perhaps five or ten, on each occasion, and counting the numbers of animals caught.

Plant zones are best examined by hand before collecting with short jabs of the net. Lift plants individually to see if there are any animals sticking to them. This is a particularly good area for the eggs of water beetles and bugs. Floating plants can quickly be dropped into a dish of water and shaken to see what swims out. Experience soon teaches what to look for. Oval pieces taken out of the leaves of waterlilies and pondweeds suggest the work of the china-mark moth. Its caterpillars live underwater, as do those of several other moths, and their presence is confirmed by finding the missing ovals attached to the underside of the leaf with the caterpillars sandwiched in between. Ragged holes in the leaf show where the caterpillars have been feeding.

COLLECTING EQUIPMENT

Very little equipment is needed to start pond collecting but devising and making nets, dredges and other gear is part of the fun. Proper apparatus can be bought but a short-handled, fine-meshed aquarium net or even a metal kitchen sieve are suitable for casual collecting. A small net is handy and inconspicuous. It can be carried as a permanent fixture in a car and slips readily into bag or pocket, thereby avoiding the old image of the eccentric naturalist armed with butterfly net.

A simple all-purpose net can be made from discarded nylon tights or stockings, cut about thigh level to give the right dimensions. Sew this to a ring of stout galvanised wire, or simply wrap the nylon over the wire and glue it. Leave spare wire at each end of the ring so that it can be stapled or lashed to a pole. For a smaller net, the wire can be twisted around itself in a spiral to make a short handle. The bottom of the nylon tube is gathered to make a bag. Instead of a length of stocking, a shopping bag of finely meshed plastic can be used. This sort of net is too flimsy for working through dense mats or stands of water plants, when a more professional iron-framed net is needed, but it is satisfactory for open water and can be converted into a plankton net by securing a small glass bottle to the bottom of the stocking tube with a rubber band. Small animals, such as water fleas, are washed into the tube as the net drains and each catch can be inspected by holding up the bottle. Repeated sweeps add to the numbers and give a concentrated catch.

Little more collecting equipment is needed by the average pond collector. The activities of animals living underwater are often obscured by surface reflection and ripples but this problem can be overcome with a glass-bottomed viewing box. Either make a wooden box, waterproof it and fit a suitable sheet of glass in the bottom, or find the glass then make the necessary box, thereby avoiding a delicate glass-cutting operation. An old glazed picture frame is a good start. The box can be built onto the sides of the frame and waterproofing is simple. An easier

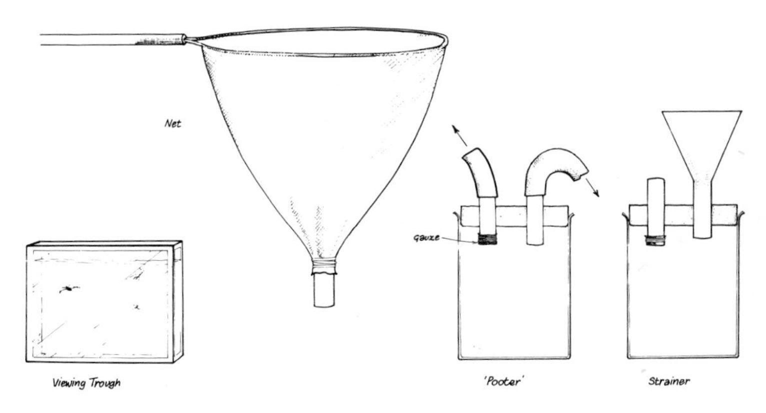

38 Collecting equipment

alternative is to remove both ends of a large tin can and tie a sheet of clear polythene firmly over one end.

Mud-living animals can be dredged out with a strong framed net or a kitchen sieve but the collection of deep-water plants is assisted by a grapnel or drag made of stout wire bent into prongs and inserted into a short length of metal tubing which is hammered flat. The drag is attached to a line, thrown into the pond so that it snags the required specimen and is pulled back.

A useful gadget for picking up individual animals is the entomologist's aspirator, better known as a 'pooter'. This is a glass jar with two tubes leading through the cork. One tube is put in the mouth, the other placed close enough to the required animal for a sudden intake of breath to suck it up. A small piece of gauze on the mouth tube prevents the insect being swallowed. Although usually used for land insects, the pooter can be adapted for use in water.

A white plastic tray or pie dish is needed at the waterside for sorting the catch. Plants can be sifted and the animals examined, then transferred to suitable containers with the aid of a camel-hair paint brush for soft-bodied larvae, forceps for hard-bodied insects and an eye-dropper for small crustaceans. A jamjar and a viewing trough are convenient for eye-level examination of the catch. The viewing trough is made from two small panes of glass with a U-shaped piece of rubber or plastic sandwiched between them and glued together with silicone cement. The trough keeps small animals in a narrow vertical plane so that they can be examined easily with a hand lens.

Within a very short time a mass of varied plants and animals will be accumulated. There is such an embarrassment of riches that the task of examining them can be quite off-putting. Now is the time to make the preliminary inspection and to throw back all that is not wanted for further study. It is well to remember that the increased popularity of field studies is seriously affecting some animals and plants. Everyone now knows that collecting birds' eggs is a bad thing but few realise how damaging other forms of collecting can be. The disappearance of the giant water beetle is probably due to its popularity as an aquarium animal, so all pond collectors should remember that someone has probably visited the pond before them and that they will not be the last to sample it. Parties of students, in particular, must be familiar with the Conservation Code when they descend on a pond.

1 Examine all larger species at the waterside and return them as soon as possible.
2 Take no more specimens home than is absolutely necessary. Keep them in cool conditions and return them to the pond.
3 If a party is working together, make one person responsible for keeping specimens.
4 If stones and logs have been overturned for examination, replace them as they were.
5 Return all water plants that have been examined for animals.
6 Avoid trampling the margins and stirring up mud.

Leave the place as it was.

Remember that the pond is someone's home!

Any specimens that are required for further study should be placed in proper containers, remembering to keep species separate so that they do not eat each other. Glass or plastic screwtop bottles are best for small animals but polythene bags are easily carried and useful. Pack the animals with damp vegetation or a little water and secure the bag by twisting its neck, folding it over and making fast with a rubber band. The bulk of the water in samples of crustaceans and other small animals can be reduced by a strainer. This is a wide-necked jar whose cork is fitted with a funnel and an outlet tube covered with gauze. The original sample is poured into the funnel and excess water passes through the outlet, leaving the animals behind.

After the initial survey, what next? Collecting can develop in two ways; either by continuing to do basic collecting on a number of ponds, perhaps concentrating on certain species, or making special studies. Natural history in Britain is such a rich, rewarding subject because the island's geology is so complex. Within a few miles' radius the soil can change quite radically, from sand or clay to chalk or lime. The changes are reflected in the flora and, perhaps less spectacularly, in the fauna. So apart from the casual variation from pond to pond, and from time to time, there may also be more regular trends that depend on underlying soil or on shelter, depth, access by farm animals which add fertiliser, and so on.

The alternative to general surveys is the narrow, specialist study on a particular animal or plant group, for instance caddis flies (p 57). Such a study is most likely to arise naturally out of the general survey, when a point of interest crops up and becomes worthy of further investigation to answer the questions when? where? why? and how?

Traps are useful for catching samples of particular animals. Quite a degree of ingenuity can go into the lobster-pot type. The simplest is the wine bottle with the centre of its inverted bottom knocked out with a sharp blow to make a funnel that allows animals in but not out. This is the basic 'minnow trap'. Choice of bait determines what will be caught. A cabbage leaf, for instance, will attract plant-eating caddis larvae and snails, also tadpoles and worms. A sophisticated form of lobster pot in which a large tin can or section of drainpipe has a gauze funnel mounted at one end and is closed with a block of wood at the other, utilises the attraction of water fleas by light. On the inside of the block a small torch is mounted inside a screw-top jar to attract the water fleas.

Adult insects can be caught with a floating net as they emerge from the pond. Construct a square frame, equipped with floats and covered with a tent of muslin or fine-meshed nylon cloth, so that the apparatus looks like a floating meat safe. Anchored in a pond, lake or even in a stream, this will trap emerging insects, such as mayflies, dragonflies and midges, which can then be picked out with a pooter.

The 'meat-safe' can be anchored over a variety of aquatic habitats. For instance shallow water yields different insects from deep water. There are also differences in insects collected over muddy and stony bottoms and from over different kinds of water plants. A few insects emerge at any time during day or night but frequent checking of the trap shows that many emerge within narrow limits. Some appear at midday while others prefer dusk. Again, some insects emerge at certain times in spring and summer. When the emergence pattern for an insect has been deciphered, it is then worth taking a closer look at the right time to watch the individuals appear at the surface and to see how they escape into the air.

11

THE INDOOR POND

The trouble with exploring a pond by net and dredge is that the animals we collect have been torn from their homes. The haul results in a kicking, struggling mass of little animals strained from their watery environment. We can get little idea of what they were doing before their lives were so rudely interrupted. Even watching quietly from the pond's edge and perhaps using a viewing box is only getting us a little further. Too much is happening in the privacy of the tangled mass of weeds, so the only way we can really peer into the private lives of pond animals is to take them captive and keep them at home.

There are two main ways of doing this. One is to obtain a formal glass-sided tank, a proper aquarium if you like, and the other is to assemble a collection of jars, bottles and dishes, borrowed maybe from a kitchen, to be used for a particular purpose and then returned to proper duties. The formal aquarium has many advantages, being virtually a miniature indoor pond, a self-contained world brought indoors where the activities of its inhabitants can be studied at leisure.

A successful aquarium is a marvellous addition to the home environment, an ever-changing live show that can rival television for entertainment. Fish swimming against a brightly lit backdrop of pond plants are soothing and peaceful, almost hypnotic, but a note of drama may be injected if the aquarium contains predatory water beetles or dragonfly larvae.

There is an art in setting up and maintaining the aquarium so that it stays as an attractive part of the furniture and does not become an eyesore, the equivalent of a derelict pond rather than an ornamental pool. If we accept this, it is not possible to give more than the basic outlines of the techniques any more than instructions can be given for fitting out a pond. The rest has to be learned by experience of many trials; of aquaria that end up as stinking soups, of aquaria that are as clear as a bell but devoid of life, and of some that blossom and flourish. The aquarist's hobby is made much easier today by the hardware that can be bought over the shop counter.

Modern silicone rubber cement has provided the answer to leaking tanks. It comes in handy tubes so there is no problem of mixing and application. It is flexible when dry so the frame of the aquarium need not be rigid and can be of light metal strip, as the cement adheres to glass. In fact, the adhesion is so good that small aquaria can be made simply by glueing sheets of glass together. A good layer of cement is sandwiched between sheets, the surplus is cleaned off on the outside but moulded into the back of the joint to ensure a continuous waterproof run that reinforces the strength of the joint. The sheets of glass are held together by sticky tape until the cement is dry enough to hold the panes together, but the new aquarium should not be filled for 48 hours, to allow complete curing. Small aquaria can be made for a particular purpose, or to fit on a table top or window ledge. If some old window panes can be acquired, the saving is immense and gives a great feeling of achievement.

Before proceeding further, it would be wise to take the aquarium outdoors, or stand it in a sink, and quickly fill it. Wipe the outside dry and watch for signs of leaks. A short time spent checking saves later trouble in the form of wet carpets and stranded animals. The position of the aquarium must then be chosen with care. Once filled, a large aquarium cannot be moved and it is well to remember the weight of water and to choose a solid foundation. The problem of lighting is discusssed on page 121, but bear it in mind when positioning the tank.

The aquarium can now be set up. First line the bottom with a layer of sand 1–2in deep. If the sand is taken from a river, sand-pit or builder's yard, it must be washed. Place a clean bucket under a fast-running tap and throw in the sand, a handful at a time. Meanwhile keep the water swirling with a stick and continue until the water flowing out of the bucket is perfectly clear. The final test of cleanliness is to stand a drop of the water in a saucer on top of a radiator. The sand is clean if the water evaporates, to leave no more dry residue than a similar amount of tap water. It could be argued that this is a waste of time because the sand is going to get filthy from the excreta of the aquarium's occupants, but clean sand means that the water will at least start clear. There is inevitably some disturbance to the sand when water is added, but this can be kept to a minimum by running a slow stream of water through a rubber tube and placing a piece of cloth or newspaper under the jet so that this gentle flow does not stir up the sand. When the tank has a few inches of water, filling can be speeded by pouring in beakerfuls of water, carefully immersing the beaker and emptying it slowly so that the water does not rush to the bottom. Rain is a good source of water. If tapwater is used, let it stand for several days so that the chlorine used in purification can disperse.

When the tank has been filled, it is time to consider the life-support system. The aquarium can be self-supporting so that the respiratory needs of the animals are balanced by the oxygen given off by the aquarium flora and the oxygen absorbed at the water surface. In practice, it is best to ignore the former supply, as the contribution of water plants to the oxygen supply is much less than is traditionally supposed. Instead, calculate how much animal life the aquarium can contain from the surface area of the water. The volume of water is unimportant, which is why the traditional goldfish bowl is to be avoided. It has a very small surface for oxygen absorption for its size and should be used only if half-filled with water. A general guideline to the holding capacity of an aquarium is that each inch of fish, excluding tailfin, requires 20sq in of water surface, so a tank 20in long by 10in wide can support 10in of fish. These can be made up of ten 1in fishes, five 2in fishes or one 10in fish. Any more and the tank is overstocked and the fishes suffer. They do not grow and surface to gulp air to try to make good the oxygen deficiency.

Stocking rates can be at least doubled by artificially increasing the water surface through aeration. Bubbling air through the water by means of a pump and a 'stone' – a cube of porous material – works not by forcing air into the water but by providing bubbles from which oxygen can be absorbed. Many small bubbles are better than a few big ones because the smaller bubbles provide a larger surface area for a given volume of air.

The lighting of the aquarium must not be overdone. Most pond animals shun bright light, yet a poorly lit aquarium fails as a source of entertainment. If the aquarium is to be lit naturally it should be placed by a window which does not catch full sunlight. Apart from upsetting the more retiring animals, direct sunshine can heat a small aquarium to a dangerous degree and promotes the growth of algae that turn the water into green soup or form a green veil over the glass. Direct light can be reduced by shading the exposed sides of the aquarium with sheets of paper, leaving only one pane for viewing. If the aquarium is to stand away from the window it can be lit artificially. Shop-bought tanks can be fitted with metal lids that house a light, but suitable substitutes can be made from plywood. Even if no lighting is required, the aquarium needs a cover. A sheet of glass keeps dust and cats out as well as preventing beetles and bugs from flying away.

The aquarium is now ready for stocking, a process that depends largely on the availability of animals and plants and the whim of the aquarium keeper. If the aim is to make a miniature pond environment with the inmates living in harmony, it is clearly inadvisable to add predaceous dragonfly nymphs to the stock. Yet these predators can provide a source of entertainment on a par with the gladiatorial spectacles of the Roman Empire – dragonfly nymph versus tadpole has the certain outcome of a contest between lion and Christian. For its own sake, this is a waste of tadpoles but, when coupled with the hope of keeping the nymph alive and seeing the adult dragonfly emerge, the carnage becomes worthwhile.

The composition of the aquarium needs some thought then if we are to avoid one species eliminating another. However, it is worth remembering that the natural pond is not a stable environment and that its composition is always changing. Animals come and go as their breeding seasons wax and wane, or for no apparent reason. The aquarium is also subject to change and, as most pond animals die or go into hibernation, a 'pond' aquarium is almost as seasonal as pond collecting. Building up the stock is best done gradually.

If a local pond is being transferred in miniature to the aquarium, it is best to fill the aquarium with water from that pond. Then you can be certain that it is suitable for both plants and animals, although a problem occurs if the pond water is cloudy through mud, algae and so on. The first step is to set the plants in place. It may be easiest to do this before the tank is fully filled, so that the roots can be given a chance to secure themselves before being strained by the buoyancy of the leaves. Shallow water certainly makes planting easier but if the plants have to be renewed after the aquarium is established, two long sticks are a useful tool to push the roots into the sand. While one is used to hold the plant down, the other is used to scoop sand over it. A small strip of lead folded around the base of the stem, or a stone placed on top of the roots, helps to keep the plant in place. A useful ploy is to root the plants in small pots so that they can be removed for pruning or for cleaning the tank.

The *Potamogeton* pondweeds are good rooted plants for the aquarium, together with Canadian pondweed, hornwort and water milfoils. The last three grow pale and 'leggy' if the light is bright, but they do not need to be rooted and will provide plenty of shelter for a variety of animals. Water moss or willow moss is another good plant for cover. As it grows on stones, it can be easily lifted and transferred to the aquarium. Many of these plants will soon become tatty from being chewed by the resident animals, so they will need replacing from time to time. Duckweeds are good fish food but no use if you want to look down into the aquarium. If it can be found, bladderwort makes an interesting addition to the flora.

SOME GOOD ANIMALS

There are many good standard animals which thrive happily in aquaria without fear of their eating others or themselves being eaten. Snails are valuable in helping to clear up algal encrustations and detritus from the bottom. Their habits are surprisingly interesting for such slow-moving animals but they tend to eat water plants and the small snails are eaten by fish. Strategy in this case depends on which part of the food chain is easiest to replace – the snails or the plants. Some caddis larvae are scavengers but, again, they are liable to eat the stems of rooted plants. Useful members of any aquarium community are the various bugs and beetles excepting perhaps, the most voracious. Their great assets are their activity and their reliance on atmospheric air for breathing. Since they come to the surface for air, they need not be considered when determining how many animals the aeration of the water can support.

The same holds for newts. These are charming aquarium animals. The males in breeding dress are spectacular and they are easy to keep, requiring the occasional piece of meat or worm. If caught early in the season, courtship and egg-laying can be watched. As we have seen in Chapter 7, the courtship of newts is quite unlike the unlovely pushing and jostling competition of male toads. The dancing newts take no notice of an audience and performances are frequent. Egg-laying is as delicate as courtship and because the female wraps each egg in a leaf singly, this activity may also be watched at leisure. Canadian pondweed is suitable for wrapping up the eggs. Sometime later the larvae (no one seems to call them tadpoles) emerge as miniature newts and provision must be made for them to climb out of the water. At the end of summer, or earlier if they become boring, adult newts can be returned to their home pond. During their captivity some, at least, will have moulted. Some-

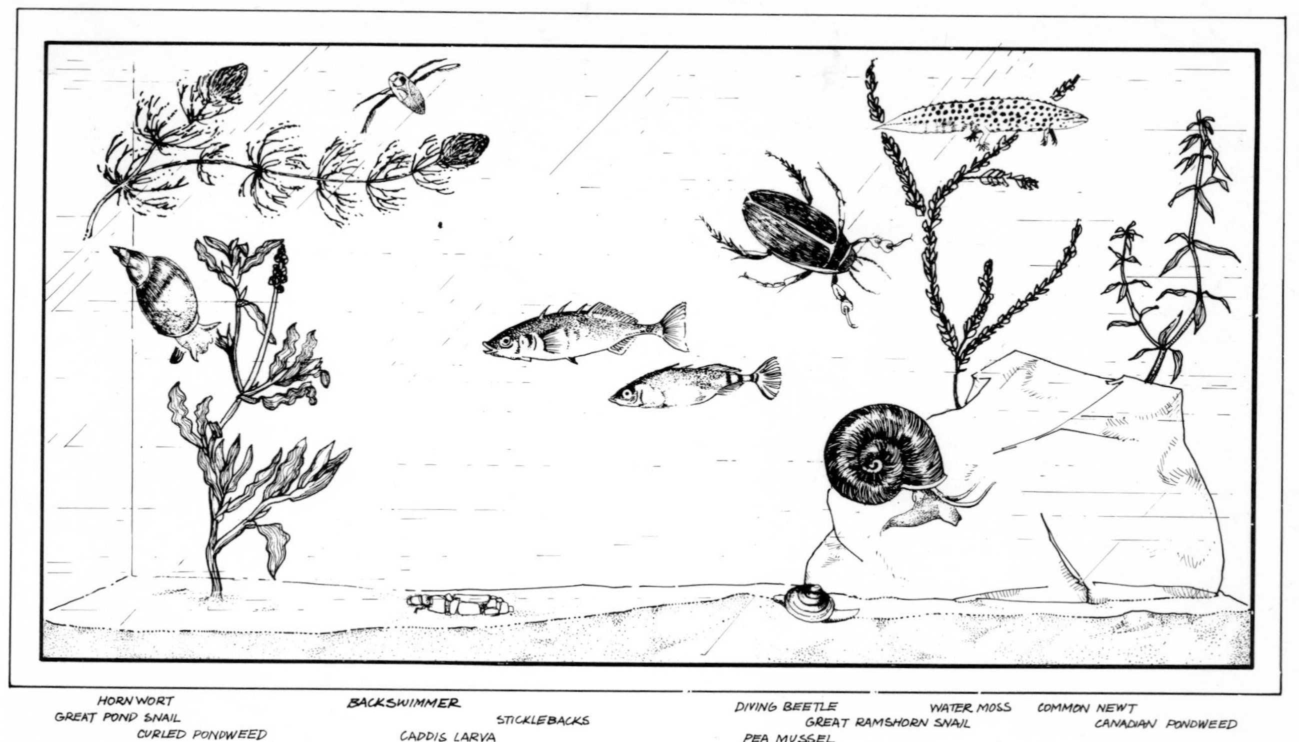

39 An aquarium

times they wriggle out of their skins so neatly that a transparent ghost newt is left floating in the water.

Non-predatory insect larvae, such as caddis flies and mayflies, are an inoffensive addition to the aquarium. Caddis flies are particularly interesting as their house-building can be watched (p 57), but in the 'pond' aquarium where animals are left to their own devices, the main interest is to watch adult insects. Suitable sticks should be stuck into the sand so that larvae can climb out of the water and shed their adolescent skins.

Finally, no aquarium is complete without some fishes. The problem of stocking density has been discussed. The fish will not grow if they are too closely packed and artificial aeration is definitely a good idea. Sticklebacks and minnows are easily kept and the former are particularly interesting if they can be persuaded to breed (Chapter 6).

For reasons already stated, the big 'pond' aquarium has its limitations in that some animals cannot be introduced because they will destroy others. Yet these are often the animals that are most interesting to watch, so they are best kept in isolation. Others are too small to be seen properly in a large tank. They can be kept in small tanks made up with silicone cement, or in improvised containers such as large jamjars. Round-sided containers are not so effective because of distortion. Shallow trays are good for observing bottom-living animals such as insect nymphs and they can be lined with gravel or mud which has no place in an aquarium as the gravel collects debris, leading to fouling, and mud is easily stirred to cloud the water. Animals kept in a small container can be given a piece of rootless water plant such as hornwort for shelter. They must be kept away from direct sunlight as small volumes of water heat up very quickly.

The charm of many of these aquarium animals is that they become tame. The inducement is food, as with taming many animals. Water spiders soon learn to associate an approaching human figure with food and they will swim up to the surface to take a fly or piece of ox heart held in tweezers. Crayfish learn to reach up with their pincers to take food and even newts will eventually take worms or worm-shaped slivers of meat. The food has to be jerked slightly to and fro because newts, like frogs and toads, react only to moving objects.

CARE AND MANAGEMENT

If fishes, newts and other flesh-eaters are to be kept successfully, they have to be fed correctly. The rule here is 'little and often' and care must be taken not to leave uneaten food in the aquarium. As the aquarium is much smaller than a pond, it cannot provide a bulk food supply, so a complete closed system is impossible and food must be introduced. Natural, living food is the best and, if there is a convenient pond nearby, *Daphnia* will be easily obtained. Unfortunately, the numbers of *Daphnia* in a pond fluctuate. Sometimes they are so abundant that their swarms colour the water rusty red but at other times they are hard to find. The remedy for the fluctuating food supply is to produce your own 'battery *Daphnia*' in a separate tank or bowl. They thrive on the very green algae that are such a nuisance in the aquarium. If you do not already have an opaque aquarium that needs its water changing, suitable conditions for growing *Daphnia* can be made by steeping a mixture of horse (or other) manure and rotting leaves in a bowl left in bright daylight, although too bright a light is harmful to the *Daphnia*.

Other fresh foods for fishes include mosquito larvae, freshwater shrimps and *Tubifex* worms. The last can be found in red wriggling masses on the mud of polluted rivers (p 35). Indeed, *Tubifex* may be the only form of life present as it can survive very low oxygen concentrations. The worms can be kept in a bucket under a trickling tap, the continuous flow keeping the water from becoming too foul even for *Tubifex*. If the flow stops, the whole mass degenerates into a putrid, stinking soup. In any case, the worms are best washed in a fine sieve under running water before being put in the aquarium.

If culturing live food is too much of a problem, prepared

fish food is much easier. This can be bought at a pet shop, but for those who are really keen on 'do-it-yourself', fish food can be made from dogmeal. In emergency, dogmeal alone will do. Grind the meal into crumbs and sieve out the fine powder which will foul the water unless there are very small fish to eat it. For permanent feeding, mix some tinned cat food with the meal and stir in a mixture of water and beaten egg to bind it into a dough. Spread the dough on a plate and leave to dry. It can then be ground into particles of a suitable size.

If the aquarium has an input in the form of food for the inmates, it must also have an output in the form of a refuse disposal service to remove rubbish. The floor of a well-stocked aquarium soon gathers a layer of excreta, dead bodies, uneaten food and the like. Apart from being unsightly, it is unhealthy for the animals and its decomposition leads to blooms of bacteria and algae as well as a fungus that makes the water look milky and attacks living fishes. To prevent this trouble the animals should not be overfed and uneaten food should be removed regularly, as should any corpses. The general layer of detritus can be removed by using a siphon to act like a vacuum cleaner and individual lumps can be taken out with a dip tube – a length of glass tube inserted into the water with the upper end firmly stoppered with your thumb. The lower end is positioned above the offending object and the thumb removed. Water rushes up the tube and rubbish is carried up with it. Replace your thumb and lift out the tube. The column of water will not run out until the thumb is removed again. The efficiency of the dip tube is increased if the tube widens into a bulb so that a greater volume of water can be admitted.

A general 'vacuum cleaning' once a week is good treatment for an aquarium. Siphon an inch of water off the bottom to remove remains of food, excreta and the dissolved salts which accumulate there. Replace with fresh water.

The most pressing problem of aquarium management and the one that gives the most headaches is that of keeping the water clean. Dirty water results from several causes. An oily scum can form on the surface, as it does on a pond, probably caused by decomposition of plants or uneaten food. It can be removed by sweeping the surface with a sheet of newspaper. More important fouling comes in the form of a grey or green cloudiness, caused by an enrichment with animal wastes; the former coloration being due to bacteria and the latter to green algae. Both thrive on excess of organic matter. Green algae in themselves are not harmful, but are a nuisance in reducing visibility as no one wants to stare at a blank green wall through which an occasional shadowy fish looms. If the algae actually adheres to the glass it can be removed with a razor-blade scraper or sponge. Pond snails, tadpoles and some fishes feed on the algae but they will not keep the glass in pristine condition.

Floating algae can be kept at bay by filtration and combined aerators and filters can be bought at pet shops. In their simplest form, air bubbles drive water through a plastic container of glass wool which traps algae and dirt. The wool is replaced at intervals. Growths of algae and bacteria can also be stunted by cutting down the light, either by shading the aquarium or introducing more floating plants. A complete blackout for a few days may eliminate algae. If all else fails, the aquarium must be emptied, sterilised with bleach, washed and restarted.

12

SAVING OUR PONDS

Conservation is not just a matter of preventing the destruction of rare animals and plants. Protection alone is insufficient; it is necessary to preserve the species' habitat and to ensure that it has all its requirements for life. To give an exotic illustration, the cheetah was doomed in India not only through persecution by hunters but because the blackbuck, its main prey, were also killed off. Without the blackbuck, the cheetah would barely have made a recovery even if strictly protected. Therefore we have to think of conservation in terms of habitats or ecosystems rather than just of species.

Ponds start to disappear as soon the reason for their existence ceases. Piped water and the internal combustion engine revolutionised the countryside's supply of water and power and so destroyed the need for ponds. Their rate then depended either on passive neglect or on active infilling. Ponds disappear also through neglect by the natural progress of the aquatic succession described on p 105. Unless a pond has steep sides, it becomes colonised by swamp plants which, if left unchecked, encroach upon the centre. As more mud and rotting plants accumulate the pond gradually dies. Many ponds can be seen in the various stages of natural filling-in but these have a charm of their own and still harbour a diversity of wildlife. A much sadder sight is the pond whose death is being hastened by an unnatural accumulation of rubbish. The accumulation ranges from the litter of empty tins, bottles and polythene bags that decorate any public place, or the private disposal of unwanted beds and kitchen cookers, to large-scale dumping of empty (or near empty) pesticides tins or waste mat-

40 The death of a pond. Once a shady pool, a lowered water table has drained it and it has been turned into a rubbish tip. Since this photograph was taken the trees have been felled and the pond earthed over to bring more land under cultivation

erial from road works. A farm or group of isolated houses often chooses to use an old pond as a dump. Very often the aim is to fill the pond so that it can be earthed over and included in the cultivation of a field. This policy has become more common in recent years with the switch in many parts of the country from stock to arable farming. Not only is the pond redundant, it is a positive nuisance because it hinders cultivation by heavy farm machinery.

The threat to many roadside ponds which once provided much-needed drinks to thirsty animals is that the dusty, muddy roads along which the animals plodded are now being reshaped for faster, heavier road users. There has been a steady nibbling of these ponds as country roads are widened and straightened to take a greater volume of traffic. Even if the new road does not completely fill the old pond, the remaining part may be sadly altered by the passage of the contractors' vehicles or the dumping of rubble. The tarmac itself is a source of danger because many roadside ponds were filled by the road drains. Rain flushes out poisonous solvents from newly laid tarmac and after a dry spell it extracts the accumulated layer of rubber and oil that has been deposited by the traffic.

The final blow for many ponds, however, has been a failure of the water supply. Over the last couple of decades there has been a general lowering of the water table because so much more water is being extracted from the ground for domestic and industrial use. Moreover, many fields have improved drainage so that rainwater flows away quickly. Now water drains out of these ponds instead of seeping in and they are left as empty holes, perhaps with a damp patch in the middle.

The loss of the old ponds has been partly offset by the creation of new stretches of fresh water, in the form of garden ponds, reservoirs and gravel pits. Garden ponds have already been described in detail. Not usually favoured by animals except for waterfowl, reservoirs are the homes of large numbers of gulls and are playing a part in the current increase of great crested grebes, while the winter sees a succession of migrant waterbirds. Much of the same can be said for gravel pits. Once gravel extraction has ceased, the pits become colonised by water plants and turn into a varied habitat which will support a surprising number of birds. As well as ducks, coots and grebes, gravel pits have become the home of ringed plovers and little ringed plovers, Canada geese and common terns, while sand martins nest in the vertical faces left by the excavators and many small birds nest in the reed beds.

The survival of aquatic life and scenery is being assisted also by the preservation or reconstruction of the traditional village pond. In many parts of Britain villages are newly aware of their appearance, particularly where they are populated by commuters or retired people who see the general environment of the village as an extension of their gardens, a place to be cultivated and kept tidy. The village green and its pond is the natural focus for this attention. The care given to village ponds has largely depended on local whim and enthusiasm but the growing public awareness of preserving a pleasant environment, which manifests itself in such schemes as planting primroses by the roadside or trees or roundabouts, is now being harnessed to save our village ponds. Ponds will continue to disappear but a healthy nucleus are set to survive.

SAVE THE VILLAGE POND

The organising force behind the preservation of ponds is the Save the Village Pond Campaign, run by the British Waterfowl Association and sponsored by the Ford Motor Company. Its aim is to restore and maintain village ponds by advising local people how to set about the job, if necessary enrolling the assistance of organised, able-bodied volunteers. With the assistance of specialists, the campaign has produced guidelines for do-it-yourself first-aid for ponds, but they do stress that anyone wanting to restore a pond should look before they leap. There are several things to do before rolling up sleeves and reaching for spade and bucket.

The first step is to ascertain that the job is worth attempting. There is no point clearing a pond if it will shortly be smothered with concrete, so check on road and building plans. It is also necessary to make sure that there will be sufficient water. There must be a supply of clean water, untainted by domestic, industrial or farm effluent. This check should be made carefully because normally clean water may suddenly turn sour. One pond thrived until a blocked drain diverted water from a dairy. Nothing too nasty there, one would think, but the water had been used for washing equipment and its high temperature set the pond steaming.

Where water is collected from a passing road it may be necessary to find an alternative source or to arrange a filter. A lowered water-table is a difficult problem. The pond will need to be waterproofed to prevent water seeping away and it may need a pumped supply, perhaps from a ditch or stream that now runs past at a lower level. The older villagers are a mine of information about water supply and possible causes of pollution, as well as giving interesting snippets of local history about the original use of the pond or pointing out a deep hole where a cow once drowned. The last item may save further accidents!

If the conclusion is that the pond is worth saving, the next step is to get permission for the project. All ponds belong to someone, even if they have been used as a common dump. Village ponds will be under the control of the local council and their fate can become the subject of 'parish pump' politics. Plans to clean up a pond are frequently met not just with the apathy of those who see no point in the excercise but with active hostility from a party that believes in the final solution of filling in the pond. The latter is motivated for a variety of reasons, such as that the pond is an eyesore, a danger to children or could make a car park. To counter this attitude it is necessary to show how even the nastiest remains of a pond can be revitalised by suitable treatment and turned into an amenity that is pretty, safe and educational.

Ideally, before any cleaning starts, the pond should be surveyed by naturalists to find out what it contains. This will not be necessary if the pond is very polluted, but an overgrown, half-empty pond could contain animals and plants that are at least local rarities. In which case, clearing up should be organised so that they can survive. It is quite easy to overlook important species because several visits may be needed before they reveal themselves. Some insects emerge only at certain times of the year and the water fern *Azolla*, for instance, can easily go unnoticed in the sheet of duckweed.

The inhabitants of the pond must be considered when planning the ultimate aim of the pond. Introducing ducks will effectively remove all frogs, toads and newts, so a management plan must be drawn up to decide how the pond should look and what is to be its eventual function. Is it to be stocked with fishes for anglers, or are ducks to be encouraged to breed? Is it to become a village nature trail with noticeboards and markers to draw attention to interesting features? These questions must be answered as different uses are not completely compatible, although it is possible to compromise, particularly if the pond is large. A few fishes, a pair of ducks and a corner where pondweeds and a reedbed can flourish should leave most people relatively satisfied and, anyway, a pond in the centre of a village will never be entirely satisfactory as either stewpond, duckpond or nature reserve. Perhaps the last thing needed is the 'municipal park pond' of clean water surrounded by closely mown grass. It is useful only for sailing toy boats.

The management plan also saves the pond from over-zealous clearing. Without a plan, trees can be enthusiastically lopped, hedges grubbed out and reedbeds dug up, only to be regretted later. Even fallen tree trunks and bramble clumps have their place in the overall pond environment. Deciding what is to be left untouched is particularly important if heavy machinery – draglines and the like – are to be used. As any recently cleared roadside ditch will show, tractors need room for manoeuvre, so the surrounding land will be ploughed. Many old ponds are surrounded by a ring of trees, particularly of willows. These would have been coppiced or pollarded, ie trimmed at intervals to provide wood for a number of purposes. When left, they grow up, shading the pond and filling it with their fallen leaves, so they must be cut back sufficiently to let in light yet still give shelter.

Timing the operation needs some thought. It is wise to make a start while enthusiasm is still running high. Summer is the obvious time for outdoor activities but any major clearing at this season will upset the pond life. It is best to start in autumn when many of the animals are in their resting stages, plants will have died back, the water is not too cold and winter floods have not started. The pond can then be cleaned ready for the next year's growth.

Although the use of dragline or tractor equipped with hydraulic excavator makes a quick job of clearing ponds that have been seriously silted up and choked with rooted plants, the need to preserve as much as possible of the pond's life and its surroundings may make hand cleaning a better prospect. Providing there is adequate manpower available, clearing by hand is more fun. If the pond is in a really bad condition, the first step is to dispose of the hard rubbish – tins, glass, bedsteads and rubble. Next comes the removal of sludge, the evil-smelling black or brown mud that has accumulated from years of fallen leaves and whose rotting lowers the oxygen level of the pond. Sludge can be baled out with buckets and coal scuttles and can be used as fertiliser, as can the surplus pond vegetation once it has been left to rot. Any rubbish, vegetable or mineral, should be left to drain on the bank. It will then be easier to carry and animals are given a chance to flop back into the water.

Once the physical clearing has been done, the pond should start to clean up on its own accord. The water can now circulate and oxygen reaches the bottom so that any half-rotted sludge will be broken up completely by bacteria. Water plants become established and add to the oxygen in the water so that more animals find a home.

Now is the time to start setting the pond in order and moulding it to its final shape. Water level is adjusted by arranging the inflow and outflow. The latter may require the building of a dam or overflow pipe. Then the edges of the pond need landscaping. By creating small bays and headlands the length of shorelines can be increased to give greater scope for variety. Some of the original reeds can be left and a gently sloping shore allows zonation of floating and emergent plants. Like the garden pond, it may be a good idea to have a shallow and a deep end, but the water should never be too deep under the bank, for safety reasons and because water voles like a bank to burrow into. An alternative is to dig away part of the bank to make a ledge where emergent plants can take root.

If the pond is to be visited by fair numbers of anglers, pond collectors or people feeding the ducks, some form of artificial landscaping is needed to prevent erosion. The banks can be shored up with vertical piling or with horizontal poles or planks supported by stakes. The timber must not be creosoted as this will leach into the pond and poison it. Alternatively, sand banks can be used and small piers can be constructed to give anglers and collectors better access to the centre. A large pond can be fitted out with an island by filling a square of shoring with soil and planting with willow or sallow to give shelter for shy birds.

The management of a pond is a continuing process. When it has been cleared and landscaped, it can be declared 'open' and the tools put away but this is not the end of the job. The pond's development as an ecosystem has to be guided along the right lines. As soon as work has been completed the pond will start to revert to a swamp or marsh as described on p 105. The aim of managment is to check this process at the desired point by clearing excessive plant growth. The pond must be treated like a garden and rank growth discouraged. Colonisation of the pond can also be given a helping hand by introducing waterlilies or water soldier, and by stocking with frogspawn or fish. In general, this should be done when it is apparent that there is a vacant niche in the pond community, but care must be exercised in the choice of what is brought in. It is best to bring in animals and plants from neighbouring ponds where conditions are likely to be similar and to consult experts on a suitable choice.

The choice of the best fishes for any particular pond can be investigated by simply putting in a few and seeing if they survive; but local naturalists, anglers or the fishery officer of the river authority can best give advice. The choice will also depend on whether the pond is to be seriously fished, possible only if the pond is of a fair size. Sticklebacks may be already in residence and the various members of the carp family are good candidates for any pond. Tench and roach survive low oxygen, feeding on muddy bottoms, and common carp can also survive in fairly bad conditions, whereas rudd prefers rather better suroundings. A good clump of weed, such as Canadian pondweed, is needed for shelter and for spawning and a healthy population can be maintained by feeding with proper fish food supplemented by scraps of bread. Carp soon come flocking when they have learned to associate an approaching human figure with food. Feeding may not be necessary in the winter and the fishes will soon let you know by failing to turn up at feeding time.

Ducks are rather a problem on ponds and their cousins the geese are worse. Lovely creatures to have about the place, they need little care and are lively, if a little noisy at times, but they can ruin a pond if allowed to get out of hand. Domestic duck have to be kept firmly in hand by thinning their numbers. Otherwise the pond plants and surrounding vegetation are eaten up, the banks get very muddy and the ducks' droppings turn the water into a thick soup. If the decision is made to keep or encourage waterfowl, the pond must be made attractive to them. A pond with suitable cover may well attract wild mallard and, being territorial, they will not overcrowd it. It should not only have emergent reeds for cover but such plants as water dock whose seeds are a great delicacy for ducks. Clumps of brambles and shrubs provide extra cover and food, but there must also be open ground around the pond so the ducks can see approaching danger. Cover is particularly important in late summer because ducks moult at this season and, unlike most birds, they lose all their flight feathers at once and are flightless for a period. An island, or even a floating raft, adds greatly to the ducks' security and are good places for nesting especially if nest boxes are provided. As well as any wild mallard and ornamental ducks that may be put on the pond, others may pay visits, depending on the size and location of the pond. Gadwall, teal and tufted duck are likely visitors and the list need not be confined to waterfowl. Such rarities as osprey, bittern and Slavonian grebe have been known to visit ponds well away from their usual homes.

Taking on the care of a pond is like buying a puppy. You are committed for years ahead, first to an intensive period of training and then to more leisurely years of upkeep that still require expenditure of time and money but hopefully giving pleasure and satisfaction. Neither pond nor dog can be neglected; you are committed to caring for them so, as with any hobby, it is imperative to think about future involvement before being carried away with enthusiasm. To carry the analogy further, no book on dog training can be more than a guideline, so much depends on the individual dog and the circumstances. The same holds for pond care and maintenance. If pond care could be put on a level with house decorating and be taught as a simple exercise, it would lose its point because the pond would no longer be the place for endless fascination and attraction. Then we might as well fill them up and rely on water mains. However, we have learned that ponds, even aquaria, are complex institutions, and that each one has its own individuality in terms of both human and natural history, and that a water main is no substitute. If Shakespeare could find 'books in the running brooks and sermons in stones' how many volumes can we find in ponds?

BIBLIOGRAPHY

Save the Village Pond, Conservation Handbook, 1974, from Save the Village Pond Campaign, Bell House, 111–113 Lambeth Road, London, S.E.1.

Busche, E. M., *A Handbook of Water Plants,* 1963.

Carson, R., *Silent Spring,* 1963.

Clegg, J., *The Observer's Book of Pond Life,* 1967.

Clegg, J., *Freshwater Life,* 1974.

Dowdeswell, W. H., *Practical Animal Ecology,* 1959.

Engelhardt, W., *The Young Specialist looks at Pond-life,* 1964.

Hickin, N. H., *Caddis Larvae,* 1967.

Lorenz, K., *King Solomon's Ring,* 1952.

Macan, T. T., *A Guide to Freshwater Invertebrate Animals,* 1959.

Macan, T. T. and E. B. Worthington, *Life in Lakes and Rivers,* 1973.

Mellanby, H., *Animal Life in Fresh Water,* 1973.

Tinbergen, N., *Social Behaviour in Animals,* 1953.

INDEX